A Message of Ancient Days

Reading Support Workbook

D1307279

HOUGHTON MIFFLIN

Boston • Atlanta • Dallas • Geneva, Illinois • Palo Alto • Princeton

Printed in U. S. A.   ISBN: 0-395-94700-6

                                                                                       23456789-B-02 01 00 99

Table of Contents

Table of Contents (continued)

Table of Contents (continued)

Table of Contents (continued)

Chapter Overview
Peoples of Our World

Fill in the blank spaces below with information from the chapter.

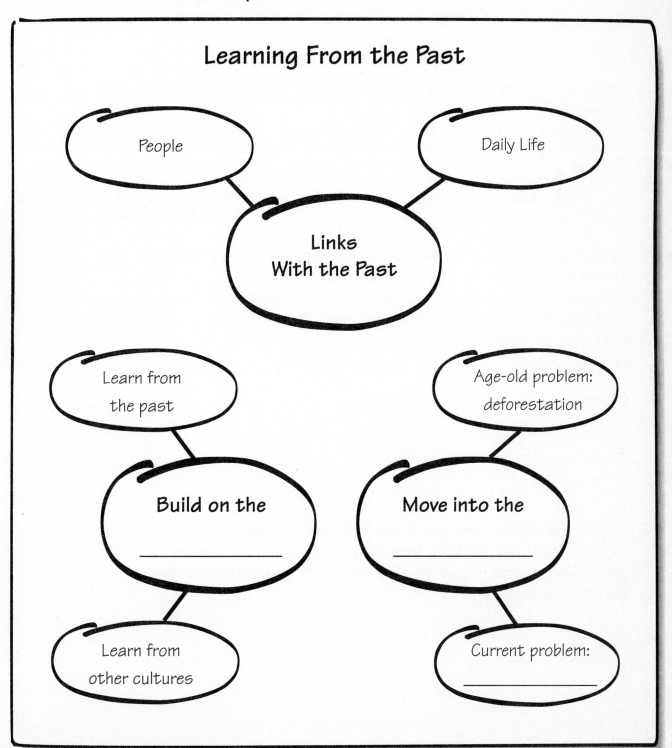

Learning From the Past

People

Daily Life

Links
With the Past

Learn from
the past

Age-old problem:
deforestation

Build on the
_____

Move into the
_____

Learn from
other cultures

Current problem:
_____

CHAPTER 1

Lesson 1 Preview
Links with the Past

(*A Message of Ancient Days* pp. 4–9)

Connections Between Past and Present

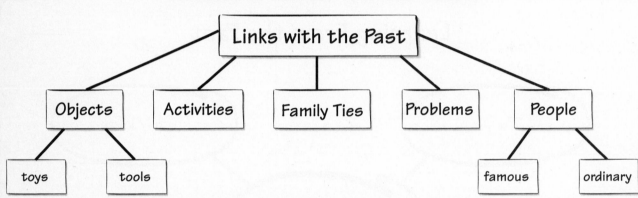

1. **Look at the graphic overview. Then choose a category from the overview. Categories include Objects, Activities, Family Ties, Problems, or People. Think about your category, and write down what things you think may have changed since ancient times. Then write down what you think may not have changed.**

   Category Title: _____

   Differences Between Past and Present: _____

   _____

   Similarities Between Past and Present: _____

   _____

2. **Look at the pictures on pages 6 and 7 of your text and read the captions. What can you learn from the pictures about how ancient people and modern people are alike? What can you learn about how they are different?**

   _____

   _____

   _____

   _____

CHAPTER 1

Lesson 1 Reading Strategy
Links with the Past

(*A Message of Ancient Days* pp. 4–9)

Finding the Main Idea   This reading strategy helps you organize and remember what you read. When you finish a selection, jot down the main idea and its supporting details.

1. **Find the subhead "Lives of the Past" on page 5. Read the paragraphs under this subhead. Write *M* beside the sentence that best expresses the section's main idea.**

   ___   You can see a mummy in Boston's Museum of Fine Arts.

   ___   You can study the past to help you understand what ancient people's lives were like.

   ___   You play under the same sun that shone on people long ago.

2. **Read "Connections to the Past" on page 7. Write two details to support the main idea stated in the first sentence of the first paragraph.**

   _____

   _____

3. **Read "The Story of the Past" on page 9. Write the main idea of the section to answer this question: Why do we study history?**

   _____

   _____

4. **Write a main idea sentence to complete the chart.**

Main Idea	Supporting Details
	People of the past cared about their appearance.
	Ancient people used many of the same kinds of objects that we use.
	People of the past had problems, just as we do.
	Ancient people cared about their families.

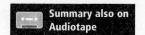 Summary also on
Audiotape

Lesson 1 Summary
Links with the Past

(A Message of Ancient Days pp. 4–9)

Thinking Focus: What do we have in common with the people of the past?

The People of the Past

People who lived long ago may not seem real to us. But the more we learn about the past, the more we understand the people. People from history were much like us. They had personalities all their own and families, just like people today.

In Boston's Museum of Fine Arts, you can see the mummy of an Egyptian girl who lived about 1,800 years ago. You can also see her picture. The picture shows a girl with short, dark hair and large, brown eyes. She wears gold lipstick. The Egyptian girl's world was very different from ours. But in many ways it was the same.

People who study the past have found objects people used long ago. Some are like things we use today.

- 5,000 years ago, Egyptians used "chew sticks" to brush their teeth.
- 2,200 years ago, Greek and Roman children played with dolls with movable arms and legs.
- 5,000 years ago, boys and girls spun tops in Babylonia.
- 4,000 years ago, the Chinese people started eating ice cream.
- 2,000 years ago, Romans enjoyed cookies.
- 6,000 years ago, women in ancient Egypt used eye makeup and combs. Men wore wigs.

People of the past were like us in many ways. As we study the past, we learn about ourselves, too.

? What are two examples of objects used by ancient people that are still used today?

*Summary continues
on next page*

Daily Life in the Past

Daily life in the past was not so different from life today. Are you ever bothered by noise? Then you may know how the man who wrote these words felt.

> *My lodgings are right over a public bath-house, and you can imagine what that means! It's enough to make a man hate his ears.*

The words were not written by a modern person who lives by a park. They were written almost 2,000 years ago by a Roman named Seneca.

Do you think families have changed? Read about an ancient talk between a father and son.

> *"Where did you go?"*
> *"I did not go anywhere."*
> *"If you did not go anywhere,*
> *Why did you idle about?*
> *Go to school."*

This was written by a student about 650 B.C. in Sumer, part of what is now the Middle East.

Ancient people had social problems, too. This gambler's sad story is more than 3,000 years old. It is part of the Vedas, a collection of sacred poems from what is now India.

> *Because of one throw of the dice I have driven away a devoted wife. My wife's mother hates me, and my wife pushes me away; a man in trouble finds no one with sympathy.*

The study of the past is called **history**. We study history to get to know people from ancient times. We learn that people in the past had the same problems we have. And we see the connections between people of all time periods and all parts of the world.

history
(hĭs′tə-rē)
the story or record of what happened in the past and why

? What are two examples of written sources that tell us about daily life in ancient times?

CHAPTER 1

Lesson 2 Preview
Building on the Past

(A Message of Ancient Days pp. 12–15)

What Causes Cultural Change?

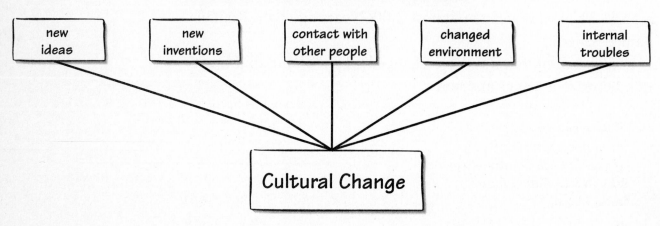

1. **The graphic overview above shows what causes cultures to change. Pick a phrase from the overview to match each of the following situations and write it in the blank.**

   a. The land a settlement has been built on is damaged by an earthquake. _____

   b. Farmers build a machine that makes it possible for a few farmers to raise food for the whole community. _____

   c. The army plans to overthrow the government.

   _____

   d. A new religion begins to attract followers. _____

   e. One group of people conquers another, moves in, and begins to mix with those conquered. _____

2. **Look at the three photographs on page 14, and read the caption.**

   a. What do the pictures show about how cultures are alike?

   _____

   _____

   _____

CHAPTER 1

Lesson 2 Reading Strategy
Building on the Past

(A Message of Ancient Days **pp. 12–15)**

Summarize This reading strategy helps you remember key points about what you have read. When you get to a good break in your reading, stop and write down the main ideas of what you have read.

1. **Read "Learning from the Past." Write *S* beside the sentence that best summarizes the section.**

   ___ Many modern inventions would not exist if inventors had not been able to build on ideas of people of the past.

   ___ A Frenchman invented the bicycle around 1790.

2. **Read the first two paragraphs of "Learning from Other Cultures." Circle the number of the paragraph that includes information you should summarize for your notes.**

   paragraph 1   paragraph 2

3. **Read "The Earliest Cultures" on pages 14 and 15. Fill in the chart with two more important accomplishments of early human cultures.**

Making and using tools		

4. **Read "Changes in Cultures" on page 15. Write a sentence or short paragraph that summarizes the causes of cultural change.**

   _____

   _____

   _____

   _____

Lesson 2 Summary
Building on the Past

(A Message of Ancient Days pp. 12–15)

Summary also on Audiotape

Thinking Focus: How have we learned from the past?

Learning from the Past

People have always dreamed of flying. About three thousand years ago, the ancient Greeks wanted to fly. They made up a story, or **myth**, about flying. They told of Icarus and his father, who made wings from wax and used them to fly.

The dream of flight began with people who lived long ago. It took many years and the work of many different people for the dream to become a reality. Like airplanes, many things that we use today exist because of people who came before us. Inventors in each generation learned from the dreams, ideas, research, and inventions of those in earlier generations.

? In what way do modern inventions depend on the past?

myth
(mĭth)

a story told by people to explain their past

culture
(kŭl′chər)

ideas about beliefs, traditions, and other things that a group of people hand down through the years

Learning from Other Cultures

Culture is the behaviors, beliefs, customs, and attitudes of a group of people. We understand a culture through its artwork, literature, inventions, and traditions. Languages are also an important part of culture.

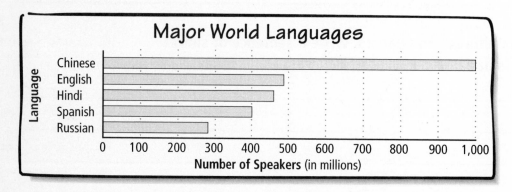

Major World Languages

Language (vertical axis): Chinese, English, Hindi, Spanish, Russian

Number of Speakers (in millions): 0, 100, 200, 300, 400, 500, 600, 700, 800, 900, 1,000

Summary continues on next page

The first human cultures began about two million years ago. One of the first things these cultures learned was to make and use simple stone tools, such as sharp-edged rocks. With these tools, people could hunt for food. But people needed more than tools. People had to learn to cooperate so they could work together to hunt large animals.

About 9000 B.C., some people began to settle in one place and grow crops. Soon farmers could grow enough food to feed themselves and other people. So others had time to invent new skills. People began living in cities about 3500 B.C. People living together had a greater opportunity to exchange ideas and learn even more new skills.

Even today, cultures are changing. Here are some reasons why cultures change:

- New ideas and inventions lead to new ways of doing things.
- Sometimes the climate changes or a natural disaster alters the land. Then people must move or learn new ways to live.
- Sometimes different cultures come together. People adopt some ways of life from each culture.
- Cultures change from within. Population growth or conflicts between different groups can bring about new ways of doing things.

Today we are still learning from other cultures. We are also learning from the cultures of the past. And cultures of the future will learn from us.

? What is a culture?

CHAPTER 1
Lesson 3 Preview
Moving into the Future

(A Message of Ancient Days pp. 16–19)

Links Between the Past and the Present

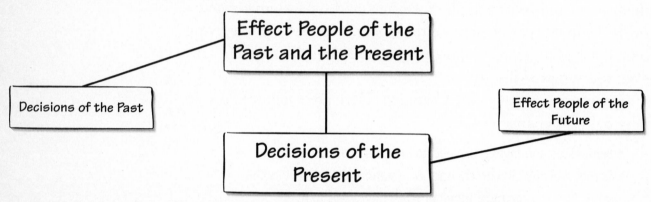

Effect People of the Past and the Present

Decisions of the Past

Effect People of the Future

Decisions of the Present

1. The graphic overview shows how past, present, and future are linked together and how decisions made in the past continue to affect people in later generations. Think of a decision that was made in the past by a family member, such as the decision to move to another state. Write what the decision was. Write how that decision affects your life today.

Decision:

_____

Effect:

_____

2. Look at the two photographs of the rain forest on page 16 and read the caption. How do you think the decision to use slash and burn methods to clear the rain forest will affect the future?

_____

_____

_____

_____

_____

_____

CHAPTER 1
Lesson 3 Reading Strategy
Moving into the Future

(A Message of Ancient Days **pp. 16–19)**

Cause and Effect This reading strategy helps you understand events and why they occur. As you read, think about the factors that caused an event. Then think about what the effects of that event may be.

1. **Read the first paragraph of "An Age-Old Problem" on page 17. Then write *C* beside the sentence that explains a cause for deforestation.**

   ___ People believe that shade is unhealthy.

   ___ Lumber companies want to grow more trees in the rain forest.

   ___ The people want to clear the land to build farms to raise food.

2. **Read the rest of page 17. Then write *E* beside the sentence that tells the effect of deforestation on ancient Rome.**

   ___ Farmers could produce more food.

   ___ Rome was flooded.

   ___ Rome's climate improved.

3. **Read the chart. Fill in the last column.**

Causes	Effects on Future Generations
Plants and animals lose their homes; may become extinct	
Land loses valuable topsoil; may become flooded	People have to move and farm new land.
Air becomes polluted when slash and burn method is used	

4. **Read "Looking for Answers" on page 19. What can be one effect of studying the past?**

   _____

Lesson 3 Summary
Moving into the Future

(*A Message of Ancient Days* pp. 16–19)

Thinking Focus: How will our decisions affect the lives of people in the future?

An Age-Old Problem

People all over the world are concerned about **rain forests.** As rain forests are cleared away, plants and animals that live in them disappear, often forever. But concern about **deforestation** is not new. Over two thousand years ago, a Greek teacher named Plato worried that too many trees were being cut down on Greek mountaintops. About the same time, deforestation caused flooding in Rome. Much of the United States was once covered with trees. The coming of European settlers changed that, too. Today, the whole world watches the rain forests and worries about their future.

? What is deforestation?

rain forest
(rān fôr´ĭst)
dense evergreen woods found in a tropical area that has a yearly rainfall of at least 110 to 140 inches

deforestation
(dē-fôr´ĭ-stā´shən)
the process of clearing away trees or forests

A Current Problem

The rain forests on a small island called Madagascar near East Africa are almost gone. Many people want the Madagascar rain forests to be cleared. Selling the lumber makes money for the people of Madagascar and helps the economy. Clearing the rain forests makes room for farms that grow food to feed the people of Madagascar.

The deforestation of Madagascar solves some problems, but it causes others. Many of the animals and plants that live on Madagascar do not exist in any other place. If their home disappears, they will be gone from the earth forever.

Summary continues on next page

Changes in geography will also cause changes in the native cultures of Madagascar. Without rain forests, the rivers that supply water for the farmers will dry up. So the land that was cleared for farming will be less useful. The changes in Madagascar will also affect the earth's atmosphere all over the world.

[?] Why does Madagascar face pressure to clear its rain forests?

Looking for Answers

Studying the past can help us solve problems we face today. We can see how cultures before us handled similar problems. We can learn from their mistakes and borrow ideas that worked. By knowing what worked and did not work in the past, we can predict how our actions will affect the future. People ignored the problems that deforestation caused in Greece and Rome. Will we do the same today?

[?] How can learning about the past help us understand the problems of today?

Chapter Overview
People and Places

Fill in the blank spaces below with information from the chapter.

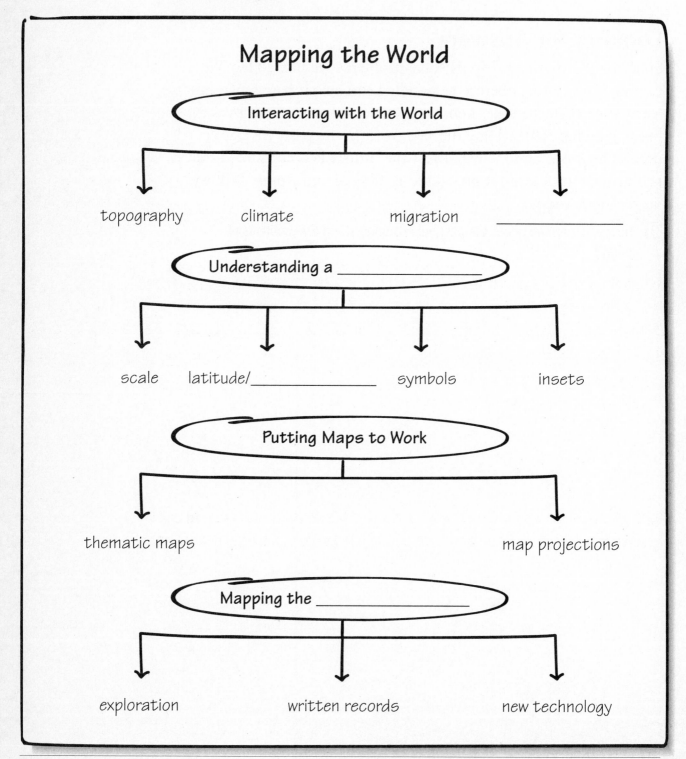

Mapping the World

Interacting with the World

topography   climate   migration   _____

Understanding a _____

scale   latitude/_____   symbols   insets

Putting Maps to Work

thematic maps   map projections

Mapping the _____

exploration   written records   new technology

Name: _____ Date: _____

Lesson 1 Preview
Interacting with the World

(*A Message of Ancient Days* pp. 26–33)

You and Your World

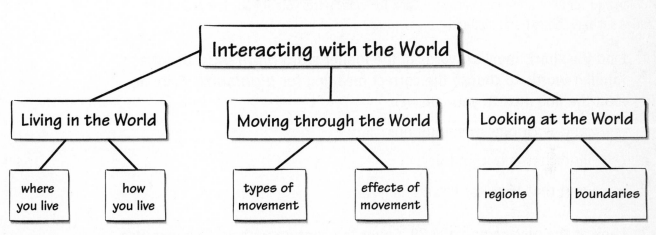

1. **Look at the graphic overview. Use it to answer the following questions. Circle your answers.**

   a. Which subject would you expect to learn about in the section called "Living in the World"?

   animals   climate   boats

   b. Which subject would you expect to learn about in the section called "Looking at the World"?

   festivals   food   boundaries between
                                                 countries

2. **Look at the map on page 33 of your text. The mapmaker divided China into five regions according to the way the land is used. What are the five regions?**

   _____

   _____

   _____

   _____

CHAPTER 2

Lesson 1 Reading Strategy
Interacting with the World

(*A Message of Ancient Days* pp. 26–33)

Think About Words This reading strategy helps you figure out the meaning of new words. When you come to an unfamiliar word, look for word parts you already know and use clues such as context and pictures.

1. Find the short, familiar words in the longer word *highlands*. Use the familiar words to choose the correct meaning for *highlands*. Write an *X* on the line next to your answer.

   ___ land with hills or mountains

   ___ land that is hot and dry

   ___ land that is at sea level

2. Look at the picture on page 29. Cover the caption with scrap paper. Use the picture to write the definition of *yak* on the line below. Then compare your definition with the definition in the caption.

   _____

3. Some words are defined right in the sentence in which they appear. Find the boldface word *regions* on page 31. Use the definition in the sentence to write a definition for *regions* in your own words.

   _____

4. Complete the chart by writing the meaning of the word in the second column. Figure out the meaning by using the strategy in the third column.

Word	Meaning	Strategy
terraces (page 26)		picture clue
geographers (page 27)		definition in text
economic (page 33)		context clue

Lesson 1 Summary
Interacting with the World

(*A Message of Ancient Days* pp. 26–33)

Thinking Focus: How do climate and topography affect human life?

Living in the World

Geographers look for reasons why people settle in certain places. They also study how they live in those places. Two things that affect where and how people live are **topography** and **climate.**

- Topography is the way the physical surface of the land looks. Land may have mountains, valleys, rivers and lakes, sandy beaches, or grassy plains.
- Climate is an area's general pattern of weather over a period of time. Temperature and amount of precipitation help determine an area's climate.

Throughout history people have settled in areas with level land, a warm or mild climate, and plenty of rain. But some people live in mountainous areas like China's Sichuan Basin. They have changed their environment to fit their needs. They dig into the hillsides to create level areas for farming called terraces.

Other people live in cold, dry, rocky places like the Plateau of Tibet. These people have adapted their way of life to fit the land and climate. They live by raising animals like the yak, which can survive the cold.

? Where do humans tend to settle and why?

topography
(tə-pŏg′rə-fē)

an area's physical features, such as mountains and valleys

climate
(klī′mət)

the average weather conditions—such as temperature, rainfall and snowfall, and wind—in an area

Summary continues on next page

Moving Through the World

If people cannot change their environment or change their way of life, they have another choice. They can move. There are three basic types of movement:

- Cyclic movement happens over and over, such as traveling to and from school or work every day.
- Periodic movement happens when people move to another place for a while, then return home.
- Migration happens when people leave their homes to live permanently in another place.

When people move, they come in contact with other cultures. Sometimes they adopt the language or customs of new cultures through the process of **diffusion**. The alphabet is an example of something that has passed from culture to culture through diffusion. Most cultures are not isolated. They owe much to other cultures.

? Why do large groups of people sometimes move from their homeland?

Looking at the World

Geographers collect all kinds of information. Then they need to find a way to make sense of the information. One way to do this is to divide the world into **regions** that have things in common. Geographers use different categories to form regions. They may divide the world by language, topography, religion, or even the sports that people enjoy. They may also divide an area into economic regions that show how people use the land to earn their living. Organizing and studying regions is one way geographers learn how people affect—and are affected by—their world.

? Why do people divide the world into regions?

diffusion
(dǐ-fyōō′zhən)

the spread of ideas, values, and inventions from one culture to another

region
(rē′jən)

an area of the world that differs in some ways from the areas around it

CHAPTER 2

Lesson 2 Preview
Understanding a Map

(*A Message of Ancient Days* pp. 34–40)

Reading a Map

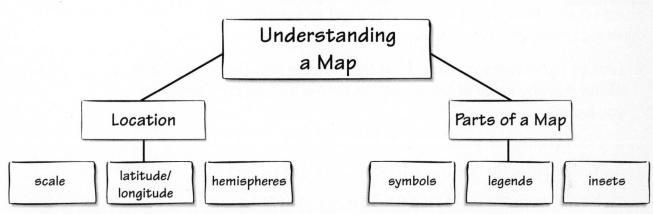

1. **The graphic overview shows things that help you read a map. Use it to answer the questions. Put check marks next to your answers. You may choose more than one answer.**

   a. Which words name things on a map that could help you locate your home town?

   —— latitude/longitude

   —— legends

   —— hemispheres

   b. Which words name things on a map that could give you more information about your home town after you find it?

   —— legends

   —— symbols

   —— latitude/longitude

2. **Look at the map on page 39. Use it to answer the following questions:**

   a. What does the symbol next to Segovia stand for?

   _____

   b. What area does the inset show in detail?

   _____

CHAPTER 2

Lesson 2 Reading Strategy
Understanding a Map

(*A Message of Ancient Days* pp. 34–40)

Using the Visuals This reading strategy helps you to use photographs, maps, charts, and illustrations to understand what you read. As you read, be sure to study the visuals and carefully read the captions.

1. **Look at the drawing on page 35. Is the museum room in the top layer of the drawing really as big as the city on the bottom layer? How do you know?**

   a. No, because the people are all the same size.

   b. Yes, because the size of each layer is the same.

   c. No, because the scale for each layer is different.

2. **Look at the pictures of the hemispheres on page 38. In which two hemispheres does the continent of North America appear?**

   _____

3. **Study the parts of the map on page 39. The inset shows the Carthago Nova area. Use the visual to write a definition of inset.**

Word	Definition
inset	

4. **Find the symbol for an aqueduct in the legend of the same map. Then skim through the chapter to find a picture that shows what an aqueduct really looks like. On what page does the picture appear?**

   _____

Lesson 2 Summary
Understanding a Map

(*A Message of Ancient Days* pp. 34–40)

Thinking Focus: What do you need to know to use a map?

The Extent of a Map

A map is a flat picture of the earth's surface. But a map is usually much smaller than the area it stands for. To make a correct picture, the mapmaker must draw the map to **scale.** Look at the scale bar on the map of the Iberian Peninsula. It helps you measure distances on the map.

Mapmakers also use an imaginary grid of crossed lines to locate places on a map. The lines are called latitude and longitude.

- Lines of latitude, or parallels, run east and west.
- Lines of longitude, or meridians, run north and south.

These lines are measured in units called degrees. Latitude is measured in degrees north and south of the equator. Longitude is measured east and west of the prime meridian.

? What do you need to know about a place in order to locate it on a map?

scale
(skāl)

the relationship between distance on a map and actual distance on earth

*Summary continues
on next page*

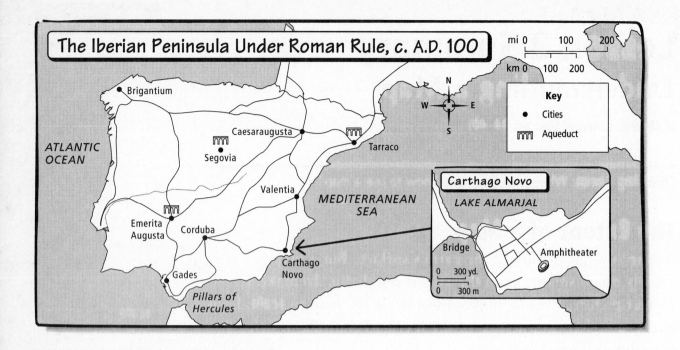

The Content of a Map

Understanding latitude, longitude, and scale will help you find places on a map and measure distances between them. But the **cartographers** who make maps also use symbols to help you read maps.

Look at the map of the Iberian Peninsula. In the lower left corner, you will find the **legend** that shows what the map symbols mean. Legends can have different kinds of symbols. The tiny picture shows an aqueduct, a huge pipe that the Romans built to carry water from place to place. The map also shows the locations of Roman towns and roads.

The smaller map in the bottom right corner is called an **inset.** The inset shows a small part of the main map. But it shows that small part in greater detail. The inset is drawn to a larger scale than the main map. Use the scale on the inset to find the distance you would need to travel to go from the bridge to the amphitheater.

If you can recognize lines of latitude and longitude, legends, symbols, insets, and scale, you can read the basic language of maps.

[?] What is the purpose of an inset map?

cartographer
(kär-tŏg′rə-fər)

a mapmaker

legend
(lĕj′ənd)

an explanation of what the symbols on a map stand for

inset
(ĭn′sĕt′)

a smaller map that appears within a larger map and shows some of the same area

CHAPTER 2

Lesson 3 Preview
Putting Maps to Work

(A Message of Ancient Days pp. 42–45)

Comparing Maps

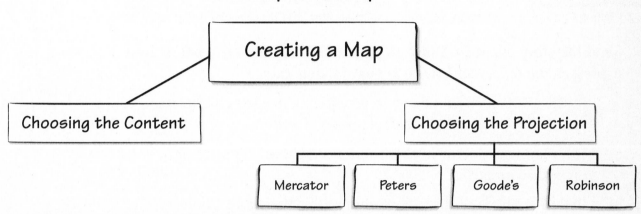

1. **The graphic overview shows decisions mapmakers must make before creating a map. Use the overview to answer the following questions:**

   a. Think of a part of the world you can show on a map. Write a title that tells what your map's content will be.

   _____

   b. What are the names of four kinds of map projections.

   _____

   _____

   _____

   _____

2. **Locate North America in each of the projections on pages 44 and 45. What do you notice about the shape of North America as you compare the projections?**

   _____

   _____

   _____

   _____

CHAPTER 2

Lesson 3 Reading Strategy
Putting Maps to Work

(A Message of Ancient Days **pp. 42–45)**

Finding the Main Idea This reading strategy helps you organize and remember what you read. When you finish a selection, jot down the main idea and its supporting details.

1. **Read the story about Dr. Snow on page 42. Which sentence below best expresses the main idea? Write *M* next to your choice.**

___ In the 1850s, Dr. Snow's map provided a needed clue to the source of the outbreak of cholera—bad water.

___ John Snow, a doctor in the London neighborhood of Soho, grew discouraged.

___ In 1849, severe outbreaks of cholera hit Paris and London.

2. **In textbooks, main ideas are often found in headings. Rewrite the heading at the top of page 43 to turn it into a main idea sentence.**

_____

3. **Name a kind of map that is a supporting detail on page 43.**

_____

4. **Read "The Shape of the Earth" on pages 44–45. Then read the main idea in the chart below. Complete the chart by writing four supporting details.**

Main Idea	Supporting Details
Projections are ways to show a round world on a flat map.	1. 2. 3. 4.

Lesson 3 Summary
Putting Maps to Work

(*A Message of Ancient Days* pp. 42–45)

Thinking Focus: What decisions must cartographers make?

Maps for Different Purposes

Cartographers use **thematic maps** to show different kinds of information. For example, a subway map is a kind of thematic map. It helps people travel around a particular city. A statistical map is another kind of thematic map. It shows data. For example, a statistical map might show the percentage of women who work in particular countries around the world.

thematic map
(thĭ-măt′ĭk măp)
a map that shows information about a particular topic

[?] On what do cartographers base their decisions when choosing types of maps?

The Shape of the Earth

Cartographers try to make accurate maps, but they have a big problem. The earth is round, but maps are flat. Imagine trying to flatten a basketball. No matter what you do, some parts will tear and some will stretch. Mapmakers face the same kind of problem.

Summary continues on next page

To try to solve the problem, mapmakers have created different kinds of **projections**. Some work better than others. But no projection is exactly right. Each one distorts—or changes—distance, direction, size, or shape. Look at the projections on this page. Compare the shapes and sizes of the continents on the different maps. Look particularly at the country of Greenland, which changes the most in different projections.

projection
(prə-jĕk′shən)

a way of transferring the curved surface of the earth onto a flat map

[?] What are some of the problems with map projections?

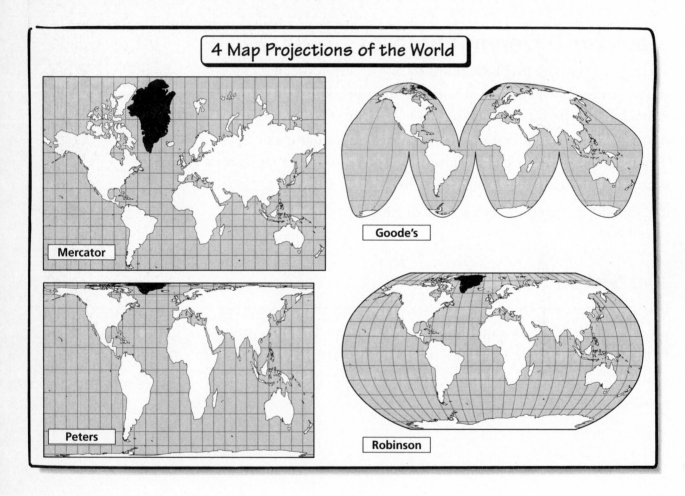

4 Map Projections of the World

Mercator

Goode's

Peters

Robinson

CHAPTER 2

Lesson 4 Preview
Mapping the Past

(A Message of Ancient Days pp. 46–50)

Linking History and Geography with Maps

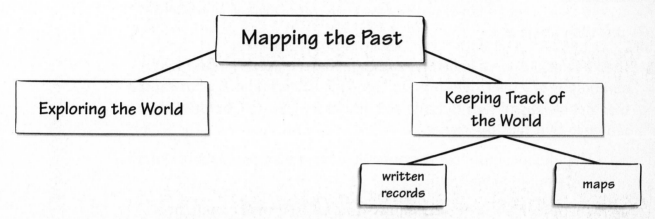

1. **The graphic overview above shows how early people began to learn about the world. Use it to answer the following questions:**

   a. Why do you think early people began to explore their world? Write one possible reason.

   _____

   b. How did early people keep track of the world?

   _____

   _____

2. **Look at the map on page 48. Name at least four cities with which Rome traded in A.D. 37. Include at least one city in India.**

   _____

   _____

   _____

   _____

CHAPTER 2
Lesson 4 Reading Strategy
Mapping the Past

(*A Message of Ancient Days* pp. 46–50)

Cause and Effect This reading strategy helps you understand events and why they occur. As you read, think about the factors that caused an event. Then think about what the effects of that event may be.

1. **The Phoenicians were known as superior traders. Read the first two paragraphs of "The Drive to Trade" on page 47 to find out what caused the Phoenicians to turn to trade as a profession. Write C before the sentence that tells the cause.**

   ___ The Phoenicians were the only Mediterranean people who knew how to build ships.

   ___ The Phoenicians needed to buy food to feed their population.

2. **Read "Trade with India" on pages 47–48. Before A.D. 37, many Mediterranean traders were afraid to travel to India. Write a sentence that tells what caused their fear.**

   _____

3. **About A.D. 37, a Greek named Hippalus used a trade route that made the monsoons work for him. What do you think was the effect of his voyage? Write E beside the sentence that tells the effect.**

   ___ Hippalus became the only trader to trade with India.

   ___ Traders who tried to copy his route were shipwrecked.

   ___ More traders used the same route to trade with India.

4. **Read "Ancient Maps" and "Advances in Cartography" on pages 49 and 50. Then fill in the causes or effects.**

Cause	Effect
	Some ancient maps have blank areas.
The compass and the astrolabe were invented.	

Lesson 4 Summary
Mapping the Past

(A Message of Ancient Days pp. 46–50)

Thinking Focus: How did people begin to learn about the world?

Exploring the World

Early explorers did not know much about the outside world. They learned by finding trade routes to faraway countries.

The Phoenicians acquired food, extended their territory, and learned more about geography through trade.

Many Europeans wanted the valuable silks and spices that came from India. But land routes to India were difficult and dangerous. Sea routes held the threat of powerful **monsoons** that could wreck a ship.

Around A.D. 37, a Greek named Hippalus crossed the Arabian Sea to India. Hippalus timed his voyage so he would be pushed toward India with the winter winds and away from India with the summer winds. That way he was able to sail to India in the shortest possible amount of time.

? What areas of the world did Mediterranean peoples learn about?

monsoon
(mŏn-soon')

a wind system that affects the climate of southern Asia

Summary continues on next page

Learning About the World

Early explorers and traders kept careful records so that accurate maps could be drawn. Some even took historians or geographers along to do this job. Alexander the Great is known for his military deeds. But as he traveled with his armies, he took along historians, geographers, astronomers, and even "steppers." Their job was to measure distances by stepping them off.

Throughout history, travelers have kept records, made maps, and invented ways to learn more about the world. The chart below describes some of the ways that people have furthered their knowledge of geography.

Ways to Learn More About Geography

Travel diaries and other written sources record information about new places.

Maps show where new places are located.

New technologies make information about geography more accurate.

[?] What technologies helped early mapmakers figure out direction, location, and distance?

Chapter Overview
Learning About the Past

Fill in the blank spaces below with information from the chapter.

Using History and Archaeology

When:
The Present

Who:
Historians and Archaeologists

Kinds of _____
• written
• nonwritten

Dating the Information
• cultural
• scientific

"Digging Up" The Past

Excavations
• _____ excavation
• modern excavation

Interpreting Sources
• _____ diffusion
• independent invention

CHAPTER 3
Lesson 1 Preview
Understanding History

(A Message of Ancient Days **pp. 56–61)**

Looking at Historical Evidence

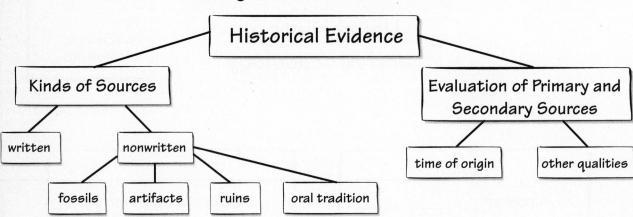

1. **Look at the graphic overview. Use words from the overview to fill in the outline below.**

    Historical Evidence

    I. Kinds of Sources
        A. Written
        B. Nonwritten
            1. _____
            2. _____
            3. _____
            4. _____

    II. Evaluation of Sources
        A. _____
        B. Other qualities

2. **Look at the pictures on pages 60 and 61 of your text. What can you learn about the volcano from the photo? What can you learn about the volcano from the painting?**

    Photo: _____

    _____

    Painting: _____

    _____

CHAPTER 3

Lesson 1 Reading Strategy
Understanding History

(*A Message of Ancient Days* pp. 56–61)

Summarize   This reading strategy helps you remember key points about what you have read. When you get to a good break in your reading, stop and write down the main ideas of what you have read.

1. **Read "Kinds of Sources" on pages 57 and 58. Check the sentence that best summarizes what you read about written sources.**

    ___ Written sources are books that were written in the past.

    ___ Written sources include anything with writing on it.

    ___ Written sources can be marks on the walls of tombs.

2. **Check the sentence that best summarizes how historians learn about prehistory.**

    ___ Historians learn about prehistory from nonwritten sources such as fossils, artifacts, and oral tradition.

    ___ Historians learn about prehistory from oral tradition, which is called a nonwritten source even if it is written down later.

    ___ Historians learn about prehistory from artifacts, which can be small objects or even entire cities.

3. **Read "The Historian's Job" and "The Interpretation of Sources" on pages 58 and 59. Then imagine that you must write a want ad to attract a good historian. Summarize what you know about a historian's job to complete the ad.**

Historian Wanted

_____

_____

_____

_____

Lesson 1 Summary
Understanding History

(A Message of Ancient Days **pp. 56–61)**

Thinking Focus: How do historians learn about the past?

Historical Evidence

People of the past left clues about their lives. Historians find and interpret those clues, or sources. There are several kinds of sources available. Some sources are written. These include books, letters, diaries, speeches, or business records.

There are no written sources from **prehistory**. To learn about prehistory, historians use nonwritten sources. Nonwritten sources include **fossils** and **artifacts** such as tools or toys. A culture's **oral tradition** is an important nonwritten source.

Historians must interpret the meaning of their sources. They must judge whether their sources are reliable. If the source is written, they must think about the author's point of view.

How Historians Learn About the Past	
Written Sources	**Nonwritten Sources**
books	fossils
letters	artifacts—tools or toys
diaries	oral history
speeches	
business records	

prehistory
(prē-hĭs′tə-rē)

the history of humans before writing began

fossil
(fŏs′əl)

the remains or imprint of a human, animal, plant, or insect

artifact
(är′tə-făkt′)

a human-made object of archaeological or historical importance

oral tradition
(ôr′əl trə-dĭsh′ən)

the stories, myths, or legends passed on by word of mouth from generation to generation

❓ What kinds of sources do historians use to learn about the past?

Summary continues on next page

The Evaluation of Sources

Some sources are more accurate than others. Some are more useful than others. Before historians interpret a source, they must evaluate it by asking questions like these:

- Who was the writer?
- What kind of source is it?
- When was the source produced?
- Where was the source produced?
- Why was the source produced?

Historians want to know if a source is a **primary source** or a **secondary source**. Primary sources are usually more accurate than secondary sources. Unlike most secondary sources, they have not already been interpreted by others.

[?] Why do historians ask questions about their sources?

The Puzzle of History

History has been called a conversation between the present and the past. The people of the past leave behind sources of information. Each new generation of historians looks at this information and interprets it from a new point of view.

History is like a jigsaw puzzle. Historians try to fit the pieces together to see the whole picture. Some pieces have been lost. Some pieces that were thought to be lost are found. And some pieces can fit together in more than one way. Historians work with the clues they have to find out what happened, how it happened, and why it happened.

[?] Why do historians study the past?

primary source
(prī′měr′ē sôrs)

information about people or events from the time the people lived or the events took place

secondary source
(sĕk′ən-děr′ē sôrs)

information about people or events recorded long after the people lived or the events took place

CHAPTER 3

Lesson 2 Preview
Examining Sources

(*A Message of Ancient Days* pp. 64–70)

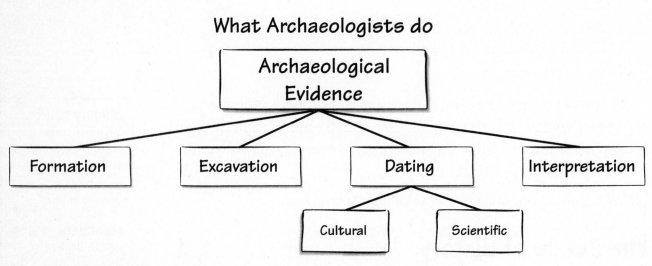

What Archaeologists do

Archaeological Evidence

Formation | Excavation | Dating | Interpretation

Cultural | Scientific

1. **Study the graphic overview. Then follow the directions below.**

   a. Name two methods that archaeologists use to date artifacts.

   _____

   b. Number the following steps in the order in which they would be most likely to happen.

   ___ Archaeologists interpret the fossil.

   ___ Archaeologists date the fossil.

   ___ Archaeologists excavate, or dig up, the fossil.

   ___ A fossil forms deep in the earth.

2. **Read the chart at the top of page 67. Why do you think archaeologists need several different methods of dating the objects they find?**

   _____

   _____

   _____

   _____

   _____

   _____

CHAPTER 3
Lesson 2 Reading Strategy
Examining Sources

(*A Message of Ancient Days* pp. 64–70)

Self-Question   This reading strategy helps you stay focused on what you read. Ask yourself questions before you read a section. Then read to see if you can find the answer to your questions.

1. Read this heading: "Unlocking the Archaeological Record." Keep your book closed as you read the questions below. Check the one you think will be answered.

   ___ What kind of records do archaeologists keep?

   ___ What is the archaeological record?

   ___ What are the keys to being a good archaeologist?

2. Open your book, and read the first two paragraphs on page 65. If you chose the correct question, you will find the answer in the paragraph. If not, review the questions again. Then write the answer you found.

   _____

   _____

3. Complete the chart by asking one question about the large picture on page 69 and one question about the picture on page 70. Then read the captions and write down the answers to your questions.

Questions	Answers
1.	1.
2.	2.

CHAPTER 3

Lesson 2 Summary
Examining Sources

(*A Message of Ancient Days* pp. 64–70)

 Summary also on
Audiotape

Thinking Focus: How do archeologists investigate ancient cultures?

Unlocking the Archaeological Record

Artifacts, bones, and fossils make up the archaeological record. By studying these things, archaeologists learn about the past.

Most artifacts are not easy to find. They are often buried deep in the earth. When a village is abandoned, wind and rain turn it into ruins. As years go by, soil and trees cover the site. Later the remains of the old village may be discovered. That is where **archaeology** comes in. Archaeologists examine the site. They supervise its **excavation**.

During excavation, archeologists remove the earth, layer by layer. Usually objects found in the deepest layer of earth are the oldest. But sometimes new cultures or natural disasters disturb the layers. Then artifacts from different times may be mixed together. So archaeologists cannot rely on just one way to date the objects.

? What is the archeological record?

Dating the Information

Archaeologists use several methods to figure out the date of an artifact. For example, they may use cultural dating—comparing the artifacts to information they already have. There are two types of cultural dating:

- Absolute dating is finding an object's age in years.
- Relative dating is determining whether an object is older or newer than other objects.

archaeology
(är′kē-ŏl′ə-jē)
locating and studying remains from the past

excavation
(ĕk′skə-vā′shən)
the process of digging up the remains from the past

*Summary continues
on next page*

Archaeologists can also use scientific dating. Dendrochronology, or tree-ring counting, is an example of scientific dating. Archaeologists find patterns in tree rings and match them to specific years. Then they can match the wood in artifacts to find out when the wood was cut.

Radiocarbon dating helps archaeologists solve many mysteries. All living things absorb carbon. When they die, they stop absorbing carbon, and the carbon they already have begins to decay. Some of the carbon is radioactive. Scientists can find out when a plant or animal died by measuring the radioactivity.

> **radiocarbon dating**
> (rā′dē-ō-kär′bən dāt′ing)
>
> a system for pinpointing the age of an artifact based on the fact that an object's carbon content lessens at a predictable rate

Determining the Age of Archaeological Finds

Method	Age Range	Process
Written records	Up to about 5,000 years ago	Use written records of known age to date artifacts found along with them.
Tree-ring dating	Up to about 8,000 years ago	Match the pattern in a wooden object to a master tree-ring pattern; count the rings.
Radiocarbon dating	From about 1,000 to 60,000 years ago	Measure the amount of radioactive carbon remaining in the object (used to date the remains of plants and animals).

? What are two methods of dating artifacts?

Interpreting the Evidence

Different archaeologists may reach different conclusions. For example, archaeologists disagree about what a famous cave painting in France actually shows. Part of the painting shows objects that could be feathered arrows and spears. Or they could be stalks of wheat. If they are weapons, the people who painted them may have been warlike. If they are plants, the people might have painted them to celebrate nature.

Over time, new evidence is found and new interpretations are made. Interpreting archaeological evidence is a never-ending process.

? Why do archaeologists reach different conclusions about the past?

CHAPTER 3

Lesson 3 Preview
Examining Archaeology

(*A Message of Ancient Days* pp. 71–75)

Compare and Contrast Classic and New Archaeology

	Purpose	Example
Classic Archaeology	To find spectacular artifacts	Excavation of Tutankhamen's tomb
New Archaeology	To learn about the lives of all people	Excavation at Koster, Illinois

1. **The graphic overview compares archaeology as it used to be with modern archaeology. Read the stories. Circle the name of the kind of archaeology the story tells about.**

   a. While digging the foundation for a city office building, workers uncover old bottles, plates, and traces of sheds. Archaeologists think poor immigrants might have lived on the site in the early 1800s. They order the digging stopped while they excavate the site.

      classic archaeology   new archaeology

   b. While trying to find the entrance to a tomb, archaeologists uncover the skeleton of a worker with a tool near its hand. They push the skeleton and tool aside to get to the gold treasures they expect to find in the tomb.

      classic archaeology   new archaeology

2. **Compare the archaeological finds in the pictures on pages 72 and 74–75.**

   a. Which excavation was most likely searching for treasure?

      _____

   b. Which objects tell the most about everyday life, and why?

      _____

CHAPTER 3

Lesson 3 Reading Strategy
Examining Archaeology

(*A Message of Ancient Days* pp. 71–75)

Evaluate   This reading strategy helps you recognize the difference between facts and opinions. A fact is something that can be proven to be true. An opinion is a belief based on what a person thinks or feels.

1. **Read the lesson introduction at the top of page 71. Then read the statements below. Write *F* beside each statement that is a fact.**

   ___ Howard Carter and Lord Carnarvon found the tomb of King Tutankhamen in 1922.

   ___ It must have seemed like an eternity before Carter told the others standing by that he had found the treasures.

   ___ The tomb had many objects made of gold and precious stones.

2. **Read the excerpt from the newspaper article on page 73. Write one fact from the article.**

   _____

3. **Write one opinion from the article.**

   _____

4. **Read "The New Archaeology" on page 73. Stop before the section titled "A Modern Dig." Then imagine that the statements in the chart are part of a debate between a classic archaeologist and a modern archaeologist. Write *Fact* or *Opinion* in the box after each statement.**

Statement	Fact or Opinion?
a. Kitchen midden is ancient people's rubbish.	
b. Kitchen midden is not worth studying.	
c. It is more important to find information than to find valuable objects.	

Lesson 3 Summary
Examining Archaeology

(A Message of Ancient Days pp. 71–75)

Thinking Focus: What can archaeologists learn from an archaeological dig?

A Classic Excavation

In 1922, Howard Carter and Lord Carnarvon solved a three-thousand-year-old mystery. They entered the tomb of Egyptian Pharaoh Tutankhamen. His tomb was filled with valuable treasures made from jewels and gold. In the middle of the treasure was Tutankhamen's mummy in a solid gold **sarcophagus.**

The excavation of Tutankhamen's tomb is an example of classic archaeology. Its main goal was not to learn about life in the past. Instead, its main goal was to find spectacular and valuable artifacts. It was a search for wealth.

[?] What was Howard Carter's goal in excavating the Egyptian tomb?

> **sarcophagus**
> (sär-kŏf′ə-gəs)
> a stone coffin
>
> **kitchen midden**
> (kĭch′ən) (mĭd′n)
> the rubbish, including artifacts and bones, left by people of the past

The New Archaeology

Today, most archaeologists are not looking for valuable treasures to add to their collections. Instead, they are trying to find out about the lives of all kinds of people—both rich and poor, famous and ordinary.

Modern archaeologists eagerly search for and study **kitchen midden.** In the past, kitchen midden would have been thrown away as worthless. Today we know that kitchen midden holds many clues about the daily lives of ordinary people.

Summary continues on next page

Modern archaeologists also work closely with other scientists. These include:

- geologists, who study earth and soil conditions;
- botanists, who provide information about plant life in different eras,
- zoologists, who provide information about animal life in different eras,
- chemists and physicists, who can help determine the age of artifacts.

Koster, in western Illinois, is a good example of a modern archaeological dig. There are no gold and mummies in Koster. Instead, archaeologists have found things like pollen, snail shells, and fish scales. These clues are evidence that there were 15 different settlements on the site. The oldest dates back to 6500 B.C. The dig has given the world valuable insights into the life of the early inhabitants of North America. It has also shown how people adapted to and changed their environment over time.

? How has archaeology changed during the past century?

CHAPTER 3

Lesson 4 Preview
Interpreting Sources

(A Message of Ancient Days **pp. 80–83)**

New Interpretations of the Past

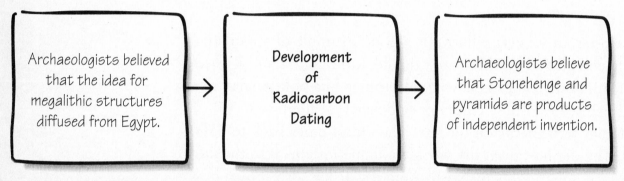

Archaeologists believed that the idea for megalithic structures diffused from Egypt. → Development of Radiocarbon Dating → Archaeologists believe that Stonehenge and pyramids are products of independent invention.

1. **Study the graphic overview. Then read the statements below. Write *T* after any statement you think is true. Write *F* after any statement you think is false.**

   HINT! A megalith is a large stone used in prehistoric building.

   ___ **a.** Archaeologists once thought that ideas about building huge stone structures started in Egypt.

   ___ **b.** Archaeologists once thought that the builders of Stonehenge taught the Egyptians how to construct pyramids.

   ___ **c.** Archaeologists have always used radiocarbon dating.

   ___ **d.** New technologies sometimes cause people to change their ideas about things.

   ___ **e.** Today archaeologists believe that the builders of Stonehenge knew nothing about the pyramids of ancient Egypt.

2. **The photograph on page 82 shows how the megaliths at Stonehenge look today. How are these megaliths like the pyramids of ancient Egypt? How are they different? (Look at the picture of the pyramids on page 185, if you need to.)**

   Similarities: _____

   _____

   Differences: _____

   _____

CHAPTER 3

Lesson 4 Reading Strategy
Interpreting Sources

(*A Message of Ancient Days* pp. 80–83)

Compare and Contrast   This reading strategy helps you understand how events or theories are similar and different. As you read about historical events and theories, think about how they compare and contrast with things you already know.

1. **Read about the theory of cultural diffusion on pages 81 and 82. Check the two statements that explain cultural diffusion.**

    ____ Most ideas were invented in a few areas of the world and then spread.

    ____ When people from different cultures came in contact with each other, ideas spread.

    ____ Cultures with similar needs invented similar ideas.

2. **Read the paragraph at the top of the second column on page 83. Check the statements that explain independent invention.**

    ____ Cultures that could not have been in contact with each other borrowed ideas through telepathy.

    ____ People in different parts of the world have similar needs and problems.

    ____ People invented similar ideas on their own to solve their problems.

3. **Compare and contrast Stonehenge and the Pyramids by writing the numbers of the following phrases in the correct box: 1) begun between 3000 B.C. and 2500 B.C., 2) built in Egypt, 3) built with huge stones, 4) built without machines, 5) built in England. *Hint:* Some numbers may appear in both boxes.**

STONEHENGE	PYRAMIDS

Lesson 4 Summary
Interpreting Sources
(*A Message of Ancient Days* pp. 80–83)

Summary also on
Audiotape

Thinking Focus: How have new historical sources and methods changed some interpretations of the past?

Evidence of Cultural Contact

Ancient Romans had contact with people from Africa, China, Spain, and India. Written records describe the contact between these peoples. Archaeologists have also found artifacts that confirm this contact. For example, they have found Roman goods and coins in India.

There are several reasons why ancient peoples had contact with each other. Trade was one important reason for contact between different cultures. Travelers also visited foreign lands. Some travelers left behind evidence of their visits. Roman soldiers scratched their names on monuments in Greece and

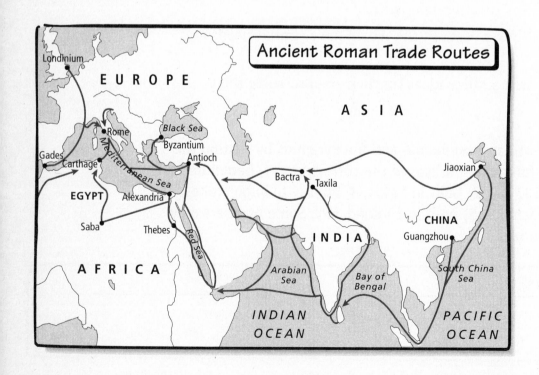

Ancient Roman Trade Routes

*Summary continues
on next page*

Egypt. Others wrote about their travels. War and migration brought ancient cultures together, too.

Whenever different cultures come in contact, they exchange goods and ideas. Some historians believe that new ideas came about in just a few small areas in the world. These ideas spread to other cultures through cultural diffusion. Other historians argue that different cultures developed similar ideas on their own.

? How do archaeologists know about contact between early cultures?

Evidence of Independent Invention

Cultures that came in contact through trade, travel, war, or migration borrowed ideas from each other. But some cultures were not in contact. Yet they had similar ideas. In those cases, each culture must have come up with the idea on its own.

Stonehenge, in what is now Britain, and the great pyramids of Egypt are very similar. Both are made of huge **megaliths** and were built without modern machinery. Archaeologists of the 1920s thought that the people of Stonehenge had learned building techniques from the Egyptians. But in the 1960s, radiocarbon dating showed that Stonehenge was built first. The builders of Stonehenge could not have learned from the Egyptians.

> **megalith**
> (mĕg′ə-lĭth′)
> a large stone found in prehistoric buildings and monuments

Archaeologists believe that some ideas were spread through cultural diffusion. Other ideas developed in different cultures independently. All cultures need to find food, to adapt to or change their environment, to record information, and to get along with their neighbors. So in some cases, people found similar solutions to similar needs on their own.

? Why do archaeologists accept the idea of independent invention?

Chapter Overview
The Depths of Time

Fill in the blank spaces below with information from the chapter.

Early Human History

When:
Millions of Years
Ago to Thousands
of Years Ago

Where:
Throughout the
World

Uncovering Clues to Our Past

Clues from _____

Clues from Geology

The Development of Culture

Making _____

Using Language

_____ and Gatherers

Homo heidelbergensis

Neanderthals

Cro-Magnon

CHAPTER 4

Lesson 1 Preview
Uncovering Clues to Our Past

(A Message of Ancient Days pp. 90–95)

What We Know About the Earliest People

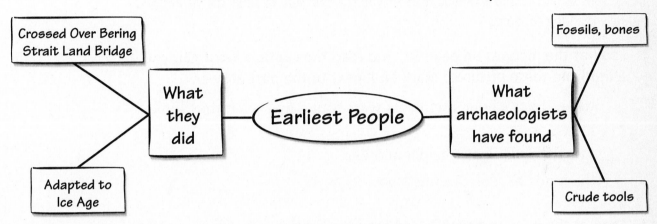

1. **Look at the graphic overview. Then answer the following questions:**

   a. What are two facts that we know about the earliest people?

   _____

   _____

   b. What are two items that archaeologists have found that give clues about the earliest people?

   _____

   _____

2. **The title of this lesson is "Uncovering Clues to Our Past." Read the captions of the two photographs and the map on pages 92 and 93. Name three "clues" about our past that scientists have uncovered.**

   _____

   _____

   _____

CHAPTER 4

Lesson 1 Reading Strategy
Uncovering Clues to Our Past

(A Message of Ancient Days pp. 90–95)

Using the Visuals   This reading strategy helps you to use photographs, maps, charts, and illustrations to understand what you read. As you read, be sure to study the visuals and carefully read the captions.

1. **Look at the pictures on page 91, and read the caption. What can you learn from these pictures? Mark an *X* next to the best answer.**

   ___ where Lucy's bone fragments were found and what they look like

   ___ Lucy's approximate height and age

   ___ the kinds of tools scientists use

2. **Look at the map on page 93, and read the caption. What can you learn from this map? Mark an *X* next to the best answer.**

   ___ *Homo erectus* died out about 100,000 years ago.

   ___ Fossils of early humans have been found in Africa, Europe, and Asia.

   ___ Archaeologists found footprints in South Africa.

3. **Study the map on page 95. Then read "The Ice Age" on pages 94 and 95. Finally, write in each box of the chart below whether the information can be found in the text, on the map, or in both places.**

Type of Information Needed	Source: Text, Map, or Both
Extent of glaciers	
Migration routes	
Movement of glaciers	
Extent of travel by *Homo sapiens*	

Lesson 1 Summary
Uncovering Clues to Our Past

(*A Message of Ancient Days* pp. 90–95)

Thinking Focus: What have scientists learned about our earliest ancestors?

Clues from Archaeology

To learn about ancient human cultures, archaeologists carefully look at bones, tools, and other artifacts from long, long ago. For example, archaeologists have studied the 3-million-year-old bones of a skeleton named Lucy. They learned that she was a small female, about 25 years old, who walked upright. Stone tools found at another site helped archaeologists learn that early humans made and used tools. Crushed animal bones and campfire ashes also help scientists piece together pictures of early human lives. As scientists find new fossils and new ways to test fossils, they learn more about when and how the earliest people lived.

? How do archaeologists learn about early human ancestors?

The Ice Age

Geologists are scientists who study the earth. They have learned that **glaciers** once covered large areas of our planet. This was called the Ice Age. Sometimes the earth's climate was warmer and the glaciers melted. Sometimes the climate was very cold and the glaciers grew bigger. These periods of temperature change lasted thousands of years.

The earliest humans had to adapt to these changes.

- *Homo erectus* learned to make fire.
- *Homo sapiens* made clothing from animal hides.

glacier
(glā'shər)

a huge, slow-moving mass of ice

*Summary continues
on next page*

During the cold periods, much of the world's water was frozen. This created land bridges. These land bridges linked islands and continents that are underwater today.

One land bridge connected Asia with the Americas across what is now the Bering Strait. Land bridges also connected the islands of Southeast Asia with Australia. Early humans used these land bridges to follow the animals they hunted into new continents.

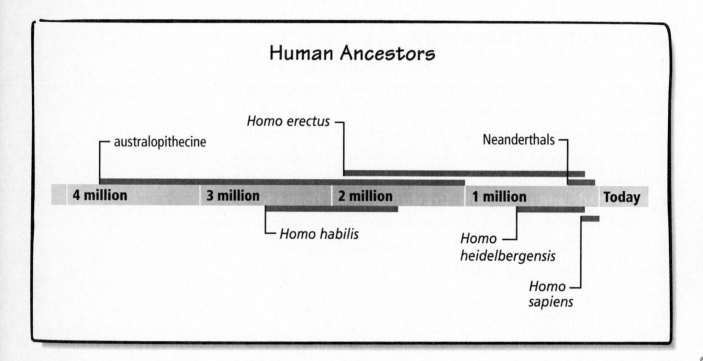

Human Ancestors

[?] What can geologists tell us about conditions during the Ice Age?

CHAPTER 4

Lesson 2 Preview
The Development of Culture

(A Message of Ancient Days pp. 97–101)

How Early Humans Met Their Needs

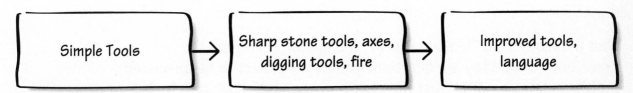

Simple Tools → Sharp stone tools, axes, digging tools, fire → Improved tools, language

1. **Look at the graphic overview. Check your answers to the questions below.**

   a. Which statement best explains the idea of the overview?

   ___ The control of fire helped humans develop new tools and a new language.

   ___ Humans always had tools and language.

   ___ Humans improved their tools; found ways to use fire; and then developed language.

   b. Which of the following developed after axes?

   ___ sharp stone tools

   ___ language

   ___ simple tools

2. **Look at the pictures, and read the captions, on pages 97 and 98 of your text. Then give the best answers to the questions below.**

   a. Which terrain would be best suited to early toolmakers? Why?

   b. Which terrain would be best suited for hunting? Explain your answer.

   _____

   _____

   _____

   _____

CHAPTER 4

Lesson 2 Reading Strategy
The Development of Culture

(*A Message of Ancient Days* pp. 97–101)

Self-Question This reading strategy helps you stay focused on what you read. Ask yourself questions before you read a section. Then read to see if you can find the answer to your questions.

1. **Find the main head "Making Tools" on page 98. Then read the questions below. They are questions you might expect to be answered in this section. Read the first three paragraphs under "Making Tools," and answer the questions.**

   a. Who made tools? _____

   b. What materials were used to make tools? _____

   _____

   c. How were tools made? _____

2. **The subheads on pages 98 and 99 can be turned into two questions:**

   a. What were the early tools?

   b. What were *Homo sapiens'* tools?

Use the chart below to list the answers to these two questions as you read the information on pages 98 and 99.

Early Tools	Homo sapiens' Tools

Lesson 2 Summary
The Development of Culture

(*A Message of Ancient Days* pp. 97–101)

Thinking Focus: Why were toolmaking and language important for the development of human culture?

Making Tools

Technology began when early humans began to make simple tools.

- *Homo habilis* used sharp stones to hunt animals and sharp pieces of antlers to dig for roots.
- *Homo erectus* made hand-axes for hunting, digging, and chopping.
- Early *Homo sapiens* made tools for specific uses. They made spear points for hunting, scrapers for cleaning hides, and piercing tools for sewing hides together.
- Later *Homo sapiens* carved bone or antler fishhooks, needles, and spears.

Scientists have not found all the tools made and used by early humans, however. Some tools, such as those made of bamboo, could not have survived since prehistoric times.

? How did early humans make and use tools?

technology
(tĕk-nŏl′ə-jē)
the tools, machines, and methods used to improve people's lives

Technology: Helping Us Live and Work

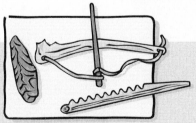

Stone Tools
Toolmaking by early humans marked the beginning of technology.

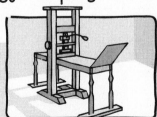

Printing Press
The printing press was an important new technology. Before its invention, people had to copy books by hand.

Computers
Computers do a wide variety of tasks at home, at school, and in the office.

Summary continues on next page

Using Language

Creating and using language helped early humans survive and develop. Language helped early humans share information, work together, and pass on knowledge and traditions. Language also allowed them to discuss how to make new tools and to make plans for hunting.

Fossil skulls tell scientists that early humans began creating and using language around 2.5 million years ago. Fossil skulls also show that the parts of the human brain used for language became larger as time went on. From this information, scientists conclude that humans had an increasing ability to create and use language.

[?] Why was language important to early humans?

CHAPTER 4
Lesson 3 Preview
Hunters and Gatherers

(A Message of Ancient Days pp. 106–114)

Communities of Early Humans

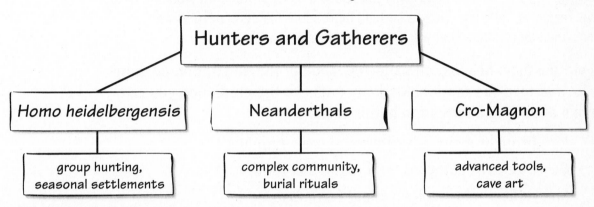

1. **Use information from the graphic overview to complete these sentences:**

    a. Two hunter-gatherer cultures are _____ and

    _____ .

    b. The _____ culture used advanced tools.

    c. Evidence of burial rituals tells us that the

    _____ culture believed in an afterlife.

    d. The evidence of group hunting tells us that the

    _____ culture used cooperation to survive.

2. **Look at the photograph on page 111 and read the caption. Find another illustration in this lesson that shows that the Cro-Magnon people had a sense of beauty and art. Write the page number and describe what you see.**

    _____

    _____

    _____

    _____

CHAPTER 4
Lesson 3 Reading Strategy
Hunters and Gatherers

(*A Message of Ancient Days* pp. 106–114)

Predict/Infer   This reading strategy helps you understand what you have read and what you will read next. Before you read a section, think about the titles, pictures, and captions. Then think about what will happen in the selection.

1. **Read the main heading on page 106. Look at the illustration on page 106, and read the caption. Mark an *X* next to the prediction you can make about the information in this section.**

   ___ Fire brought many advantages to early humans.

   ___ Early humans gathered wild plants for food.

   ___ Storytellers told stories around campfires.

2. **List one clue on page 106 that helped you make the above prediction.**

   _____

3. **Read the two blue headings on page 110. Use the chart below to predict what you will learn in each section. Then read pages 110–113. To complete the chart, write what you learned about why Cro-Magnons are called modern humans.**

	What I Predict	What I Learned
Cro-Magnon Life		
Cave Paintings		

Lesson 3 Summary
Hunters and Gatherers

(*A Message of Ancient Days* pp. 106–114)

Thinking Focus: How did human culture develop from the time of *Homo heidelbergensis* to the time of the Cro-Magnons?

Early Fire Users

Archaeologists have studied the fire pits of *Homo heidelbergensis* to learn more about how these early people lived and worked. They know that early people had to learn to use fire in order to survive in the cold climate of the Ice Age. Fire provided warmth, scared off animals, and gave them the means to cook food. Archaeologists also know that *Homo heidelbergensis* traveled together in **bands** of about 20 to 30 people.

Archaeologists have studied a campsite called Terra Amata. They learned that early people built huts from branches and stones, had fire pits to keep warm and to cook their food, and had workspace for making tools and cutting meat. It also seems that early people used Terra Amata only a few days each year, but returned to the site year after year. Terra Amata was a good place to live. There was fresh water. And there were lots of animals to hunt, seafood to catch, and plants, berries, and eggs to gather for these **hunter-gatherers**.

? Based on evidence from Terra Amata, describe how *Homo heidelbergensis* lived.

band
(bănd)
a small, loosely organized group

hunter-gatherer
(hŭn′ tər-găth′ər-ər)
a person who gets food by hunting animals and gathering wild plants, roots, nuts, and berries

The Neanderthals: Community Builders

The first Neanderthal fossils were found in 1856. They were in the cliffs around the Neander Valley in Germany. Later, other Neanderthal fossils were found in Israel and Iraq.

Neanderthals lived in groups of 20 to 50 people and stayed in one place longer than *Homo heidelbergensis* did. They probably had a strong sense of community. The fossils of arthritic and

*Summary continues
on next page*

paralyzed people show that Neanderthals must have taken care of one another. These people could not have survived otherwise. Neanderthal graves also show us that these people had a sense of community. The death of one man must have made others sad because he was buried on a bed of wildflowers. And a teenage boy was buried with an axe and food. This suggests that Neanderthals thought he might need these things in his life after death.

[?] What evidence do we have that the Neanderthals had a strong sense of community?

Cro-Magnons: Modern Humans

Cro-Magnons looked much like people of today. They used tools similar to those of modern hunter-gatherers such as fishing nets, spear throwers, and bows and arrows. But it is their art that tells us the most about Cro-Magnon culture.

Cro-Magnons carved designs on their tools. They made small sculptures out of bone, ivory, and antlers. They also painted pictures on the walls inside caves.

The first cave paintings were discovered in 1879 in Spain. They were of life-sized bison. The most beautiful cave paintings were discovered in Lascaux, France, in 1940 by a group of boys. They found huge lifelike pictures of horses, deer, and bison. The paintings may have been used as part of religious ceremonies to bring luck to hunters. The paintings show that Cro-Magnons had a strong feeling for beauty and a sense of wonder much like our own.

[?] Why do we call the Cro-Magnons modern humans?

Chapter Overview
Development of Societies

Fill in the blank spaces below with information from the chapter.

When:
10,000 B.C.–3500 B.C.

Where:
Turkey and Mesopotamia

From Farming to Early Civilizations

stored food

farming and herding

Learning to Farm

domesticated plants and _____

time for new occupations

stable _____ supply

leadership and government

Building _____ and Civilizations

culture

specialized workers

different social groups

CHAPTER 5

Lesson 1 Preview
Learning to Farm

(*A Message of Ancient Days* pp. 120–126)

Steps That Led to Farming

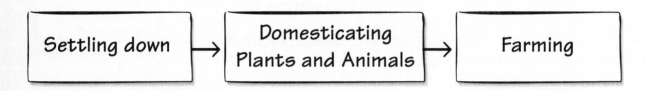

Settling down → Domesticating Plants and Animals → Farming

1. **Look at the graphic overview. List the two steps that led to ancient people changing their lifestyle from hunter-gatherers to farmers.**

   a. _____

   b. _____

2. **Look at the timeline on page 124 of your text. Use it to answer the questions below.**

   a. What was the first animal to be domesticated, or brought under human control? Where was it domesticated?

   _____

   _____

   b. Where was wheat domesticated?

   _____

   c. Which plant was domesticated first—rice or beans?

   _____

CHAPTER 5
Lesson 1 Reading Strategy
Learning to Farm

(A Message of Ancient Days **pp. 120–126)**

Cause and Effect   This reading strategy helps you understand events and why they occur. As you read, think about the factors that caused an event. Then think about what the effects of that event may be.

1. **Read pages 120 and 121. Then check the TWO reasons below that tell why hunter-gatherers began to stay permanently in one place.**

   ___ The stone mortars used to grind grain were much too heavy to carry around.

   ___ The hunter-gatherers had run out of new places to look for sources of food.

   ___ The surplus grain was precious, and people didn't want to wander too far from the storage bins.

2. **Read "Taming Animals and Sowing Seeds" on pages 122–124. What is the effect of domestication on animals?**

   _____

   _____

3. **Read pages 125 and 126. Fill in the chart with four effects of the development of agriculture in the Neolithic Era.**

Causes	Effects
Agriculture develops.	_____
	_____
	_____
	_____

Lesson 1 Summary
Learning to Farm

(*A Message of Ancient Days* pp. 120–126)

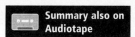

Thinking Focus: How did people's lifestyle change as they began to domesticate plants and animals?

Living in Settled Communities

Hunter-gatherers roamed the land looking for sources of food. They needed animals to hunt. They needed berries, roots, and grains to pick. When they found a good spot to hunt and gather, they stayed. As they became attached to a spot, they built longer-lasting homes.

One of the first areas where hunter-gatherers settled down was the Middle East. Here people lived in simple pits, dug below ground level. They roasted food over a central fire pit. They used stone mortars and pestles to grind their grain. They stored **surplus**, or extra, grain in bins. Mortars and storage bins couldn't be carried around easily. Once people began using them, they tended to stay in one place.

? What conditions allowed some hunter-gatherers to start settling down?

Taming Animals and Sowing Seeds

As hunter-gatherers settled down, they learned how to affect their **environment**. They learned how seeds could be used to start a new crop. They later learned how to choose the best seeds to increase their harvest.

Hunter-gatherers also learned to **domesticate** animals. Among the first domesticated animals were sheep, goats, and dogs. Domesticated animals can be kept in herds and bred for food.

? How are domesticated plants and animals more useful to humans than wild ones?

surplus
(sŭr′pləs)
more than is needed

environment
(ĕn-vī′rən-mənt)
all the living and nonliving things in a person's surroundings

domesticate
(də-mĕs′tĭ-kāt′)
to adapt an animal or plant to live in a human environment

Summary continues on next page

Farming as a Way of Life

Farming made life better for early people. They had some new worries, including insects, bad weather, and plant and animal diseases. But there were many benefits. People could:

- raise more food
- support more people on small plots of land
- live where wild food is scarce, so long as soil is fertile
- grow surplus food for trading or storing for the future

Not everyone was needed to work in **agriculture** in early communities. Some people became toolmakers, craftspersons, and so on. People began to live in villages. They learned to make pottery, cloth, and baskets. The period when these advances were made is called the Neolithic Era.

? What were the pros and cons of agriculture in ancient times?

agriculture
(ăg′rĭ-kŭl′chər)

the science, art, and business of raising animals and plants for food; farming

CHAPTER 5

Lesson 2 Preview
Living in an Early Farming Town

(A Message of Ancient Days pp. 127–133)

A Large Neolithic Town

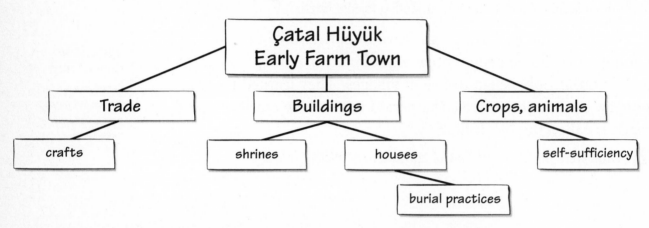

1. **Use the graphic overview above to answer the following questions:**

   a. What two things helped the people of the early farming town of Çatal Hüyük be self-sufficient?

   _____

   b. What was one product the people of Çatal Hüyük traded in?

   _____

2. **Look at the illustration of the Neolithic town of Çatal Hüyük, and read the caption on page 129. Then complete the sentences below. Use words from the box.**

smoke	streets	mud dwellings	ladders	rooftops

   Around 6000 B.C., the people of Çatal Hüyük, an early farming

   town, lived in _____. The town had no

   _____ or lanes. The doors of buildings opened

   onto _____. You can see the _____

   that allowed people to get from one level to the next.

   _____ escaped through the same hole that people

   used to climb in and out of the house.

CHAPTER 5

Lesson 2 Reading Strategy
Living in an Early Farming Town

(*A Message of Ancient Days* pp. 127–133)

Self-Question   This reading strategy helps you stay focused on what you read. Ask yourself questions before you read a section. Then read to see if you can find the answers to your questions.

1. **Read the lesson title on page 127. Put a check next to the question below that you can expect this lesson to answer.**

   ___ Why are farms important to society?

   ___ How did early towns grow into cities?

   ___ What would life be like in a farming town?

2. **Read the first paragraph on page 128. After reading the paragraph, you might wonder: What is a mud-brick building? Tell how you might find the answer to this question.**

   _____

3. **Look at the picture on page 129. Do <u>not</u> read the caption. Write a question you might have about this picture.**

   _____

   Now read the caption. Did it answer your question? If so, write the answer here.

   _____

   If the caption did not answer your question, read "Daily Life" on pages 128 and 129. Try to find the answer to your question. Write it here.

   _____

4. **Read the main heading on page 131 and the first paragraph under it. Write a question that will probably be answered in this section. Then read on and write the answer.**

   Question: _____ ?

   Answer: _____

CHAPTER 5
Lesson 2 Summary
Living in an Early Farming Town

(*A Message of Ancient Days* pp. 127–134)

Thinking Focus: What would life be like in a Neolithic farming town?

A Large Neolithic Town

Çatal Hüyük was a large Neolithic town located in what is today the country of Turkey. Archeological excavations tell a lot about the lifestyle of the people who lived there.

Around 6000 B.C., the town covered about 32 acres and had about 1,000 mud-brick houses. There were no streets in the town. Instead the doors of buildings opened onto rooftops. People walked across rooftops and up and down ladders to get from place to place.

Most houses had two rooms. One of these rooms was used to store food. The other room had kitchen and living areas. Built-in platforms served as tables, benches, and beds. Some of the buildings in town were probably **shrines**, where people worshiped. These were decorated with paintings and sculptures.

The people raised wheat and cattle. They did some hunting and gathering. There was also some industry, and craftspeople made such things as stone tools, wooden bowls, reed baskets, and woolen cloth. The people of Çatal Hüyük were quite **self-sufficient**.

? What kind of lifestyle did people have in Çatal Hüyük, and how do we know?

shrine
(shrīn)

a place where people worship, usually containing a sacred object

self-sufficient
(sělf′sə-fĭsh′ənt)

able to provide for oneself without the help of others

*Summary continues
on next page*

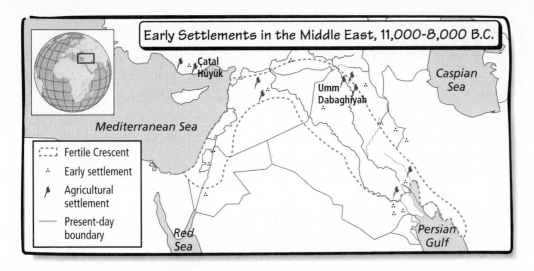

Early Settlements in the Middle East, 11,000–8,000 B.C.

Çatal Hüyük

Umm Dabaghiyah

Caspian Sea

Mediterranean Sea

Fertile Crescent

Early settlement

Agricultural settlement

Present-day boundary

Red Sea

Persian Gulf

Trade in the Neolithic World

Çatal Hüyük was a center for trade. The people who lived there made things that people of other settlements wanted. For example, Çatal Hüyük had obsidian, a black glass that was highly valued throughout the Middle East. Obsidian was used to make tools with sharp edges. Sometimes the people of Çatal Hüyük traded just the obsidian. Sometimes they traded the tools they made from it.

Another Middle East town that was involved in trade was Umm Dabaghiyah. This was a small settlement, with fewer than 10 houses. But Umm Dabaghiyah had other buildings—long, narrow structures with rows of cell-like rooms. Archaeologists think that these rooms were used for storage, and that Umm Dabaghiyah was a hunting and trading outpost.

The people of Umm Dabaghiyah hunted for onagers, which were wild animals that looked like donkeys. Hunters chased the onagers into traps, skinned them, and traded their hides. The soil around Umm Dabaghiyah was not good for farming, so the townspeople were not self-sufficient. But they did have more onager hides than they could use. They traded the hides for things they could not produce themselves.

? What was the surplus item produced at Umm Dabaghiyah, and how did the people make use of it?

CHAPTER 5
Lesson 3 Preview
Starting Cities
(*A Message of Ancient Days* pp. 135–141)

The Development of Cities

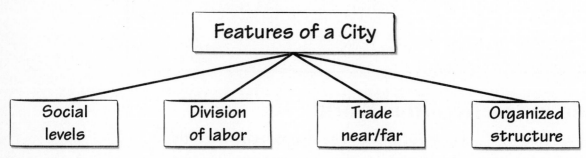

1. **Use the graphic overview above to list the four features that make up a city.**

_____

2. **Open to page 137 of your book. Read the main headings and the subheadings on pages 137–139. Which of the features that you listed for question 1 do you expect to learn more about under each heading?**

   a. Leadership and Planning

   _____

   b. Specialized Workers

   _____

   c. Richer and Poorer

   _____

   d. Trade Near and Far

   _____

CHAPTER 5

Lesson 3 Reading Strategy
Starting Cities

(*A Message of Ancient Days* pp. 135–141)

Finding the Main Idea   This reading strategy helps you organize and remember what you read. When you finish a selection, jot down the main idea and its supporting details.

1. **Read "A City on the Plain" on pages 136 and 137. Write *M* next to the sentence that best tells the main idea of the selection.**

   ___ Ur was just one of the cities located on the plain of the Tigris and Euphrates rivers.

   ___ Ur arose because of advances in agriculture and changes in society.

   ___ The people of Ur dug canals from the riverbeds to their fields.

2. **Read pages 137–139. Find and write two supporting details for the main idea: *Cities have special features*.**

   _____

   _____

3. **Look at the chart "The Rise of Cities" on page 140. The smaller circles show supporting details. What is the main idea?**

   _____

4. **Read "An Early Civilization" on pages 140 and 141. List the details that support the main idea in the chart below.**

Main Idea	Supporting Details
Civilization is a complex society.	

Lesson 3 Summary
Starting Cities

(*A Message of Ancient Days* pp. 135–141)

Thinking Focus: What are the characteristics of a city?

A City on the Plain

The city of Ur was located on the dry plain near the Tigris and Euphrates rivers. In order to farm the land, the people of Ur used canals, ditches, and pipes to get the water from the rivers to the dry land. With the help of **irrigation**, the farmers of Ur could grow barley, wheat, vegetables, date palms, and grapevines. They even produced a surplus of food. This surplus prevented **famine**. It also allowed some of the people to do jobs other than farming. As a result of irrigation farming, the population of Ur grew rapidly.

irrigation
(ĭr′ĭ-gā′shən)
the act of supplying dry lands with water

famine
(făm′ĭn)
a widespread shortage of food that threatens death

Development of Cities

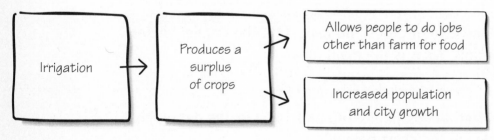

Irrigation → Produces a surplus of crops → Allows people to do jobs other than farm for food / Increased population and city growth

[?] How did irrigation make it possible for a city to grow in the land around the Tigris and Euphrates?

Summary continues on next page

Features of a City

There are several characteristics of a city besides a large population. One characteristic is organization and strong leadership. The people of Ur had to be organized to build their irrigation system. They also had to be organized to build their large public buildings—including a type of temple tower called a ziggurat.

People in cities are also employed in many different jobs. A tablet found at Ur showed that people's jobs included chisel worker, gem cutter, and metalworker. Ur also had judges, doctors, and musicians.

Cities also usually have different social groups. Items taken from burial tombs showed that Ur had three levels of society:

- Government officials, priests, and soldiers
- Merchants, teachers, laborers, farmers, and craftspeople
- Slaves

Long-distance trade is another sign of a city. Ur was located on a sun-baked plain, hundreds of miles from valuable resources. So trade was necessary for the city's survival. Priests kept records of goods that flowed in and out of the city.

? What archaeological evidence tells us that Ur was a city?

An Early Civilization

Ur and other cities around the Tigris and Euphrates rivers were part of the world's earliest **civilizations**. There are five characteristics that made them civilizations:

- Stable food supply
- Specialization of labor
- A system of government
- Social levels
- A developed culture of art, religion, music, and law

? What are five features of a civilization?

civilization
(sĭv′ə-lĭ-zā′shən)

a society with a food supply, specialized jobs, a government, and a developed culture

Chapter Overview
Mesopotamia

Fill in the blank spaces below with information from the chapter.

When:
5000 B.C.–550 B.C.
Where:
Mesopotamia
Who:
Sumerians, Assyrians, Babylonians

The Development of Civilization in Mesopotamia

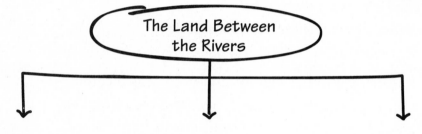

The Land Between the Rivers

Tigris and _____   irrigation   food surplus

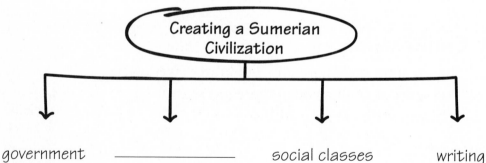

Creating a Sumerian Civilization

government   _____   social classes   writing

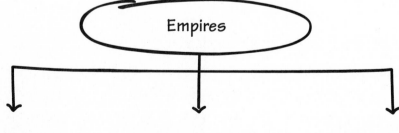

Empires

Akkad   Assyria/New Assyria   Babylonia/ _____

Name: _____ Date: _____

Lesson 1 Preview
The Land Between Two Rivers

(A Message of Ancient Days **pp. 150–155)**

Conditions Leading to Civilization in Mesopotamia

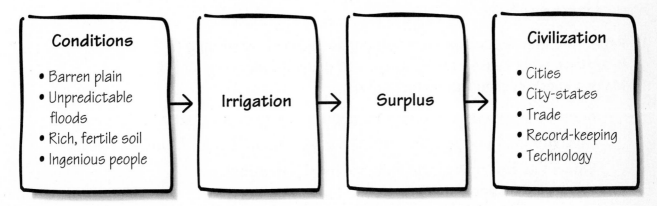

Conditions
- Barren plain
- Unpredictable floods
- Rich, fertile soil
- Ingenious people

→ **Irrigation** → **Surplus** →

Civilization
- Cities
- City-states
- Trade
- Record-keeping
- Technology

1. **Look at the graphic overview. Use it to answer the following questions:**

    a. List the four conditions that describe Mesopotamia.

    _____

    _____

    _____

    _____

    b. List five achievements of this civilization.

    _____

    _____

    _____

    _____

    _____

2. **Look at the pictures and captions on pages 154 and 155. The pictures show three inventions of the Sumerians. Name these inventions.**

    _____

    _____

CHAPTER 6

Lesson 1 Reading Strategy
The Land Between Two Rivers

(A Message of Ancient Days **pp. 150–155)**

Cause and Effect   This reading strategy helps you understand events and why they occur. As you read, think about the factors that caused an event. Then think about what the effects of that event may be.

1. **Read "The Mesopotamian Plain" on pages 150–152. According to historians, what caused the Sumerians to develop new ways of life? Make a check next to the correct answer.**

    ___ Sumer was 10,000 square miles, about the size of Maryland.

    ___ Mesopotamia is a plateau and the early Sumerians were farmers.

    ___ Sumerians had to struggle with the harsh environment of southern Mesopotamia.

2. **How did the Sumerian irrigation system change the land?**

    _____

3. **Look for causes and effects as you read "The Remarkable Sumerians" on pages 152–155. Use the information to complete the following chart.**

Causes	Effects
Farmers irrigate.	
	Priests store grain and collect taxes.
	Traders invent *bullas*.
Farmers need to break through hard clay.	

Lesson 1 Summary
The Land Between Two Rivers

(*A Message of Ancient Days* pp. 150–155)

Thinking Focus: What was the relationship between the geography of Mesopotamia and the civilization that developed there?

The Mesopotamian Plain

The name Mesopotamia means "the land between the rivers." The rivers that wind through Mesopotamia are the Tigris and Euphrates rivers. The land in northern Mesopotamia is a **plateau.** The land in southern Mesopotamia is a **plain.** The southern part of the plain was called Sumer.

The people of Sumer lived in a harsh environment. Summers were very hot with little rainfall, and so the land dried out. In spring and fall there were floods. The Sumerians had to adapt to this environment. To bring river water to the dry land, they created an irrigation system of dams, gates, and canals. To control the floods, they developed lakes and ponds to hold excess flood water until it was needed. Irrigation and flood control turned the dry land into a fertile plain, and the Sumerians became successful farmers.

? Give evidence to support this statement: Irrigation was essential to the development of civilization in Mesopotamia.

plateau
(plă-tō′)
an elevated area of flat land

plain
(plān)
a broad area of flat, open land

Summary continues on next page

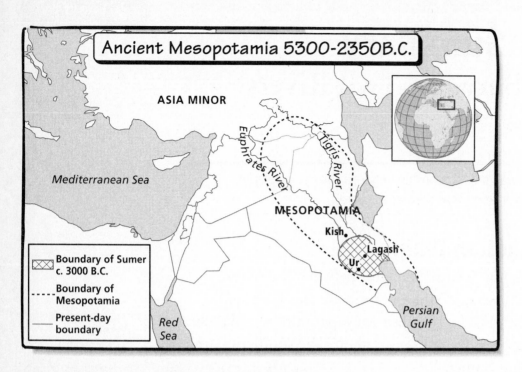

The Remarkable Sumerians

By 3000 B.C., there were 12 great Sumerian cities. Three of the best-known are Ur, Kish, and Lagash. The cities were independent **city-states** ruled by priests. Irrigation allowed the farmers of each city-state to produce a surplus of food. This allowed city dwellers to do other jobs and to trade for food.

Sumerians had **administrators** to manage and organize the building and upkeep of the irrigation canals and great temples. They traded their surplus wheat, barley, dates, wool, and dairy products for the tools and supplies they needed for building. **Artisans** traded their jewelry, pottery, musical instruments, and fabric.

To keep track of their trading, Sumerians developed a system of record-keeping. They used clay or stone tokens in a clay container called a *bulla*. Record-keeping marks on the outside of the bulla may have led to the invention of writing.

? What were some important advances that the Sumerians made in government, technology, and communication?

city-state
(sĭt′ ē-stāt′)

a self-governing unit made up of a city and its surrounding area

administrator
(ăd-mĭn′ ĭ-strā′ tər)

a manager; one who directs a government or an organization

artisan
(är′ tĭ-zən)

a worker who is skilled in making a particular product by hand

CHAPTER 6

Lesson 2 Preview
The Contributions of the Sumerians

(*A Message of Ancient Days* pp. 156–161)

The Sumerian Civilization

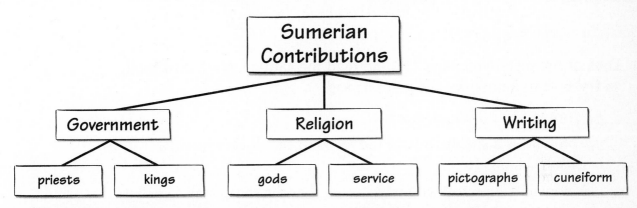

1. **The graphic overview helps you to see the contributions Sumerians made to civilization.**

   a. List the three areas in which the Sumerians made a contribution.

   _____

   b. Two rulers shared leadership of the Sumerian government. What kind of rulers were these?

   _____

   c. What kinds of writing were developed by the Sumerians?

   _____

2. **Look at the pictures on page 158 and page 159 and read the captions. Then read the following statements about the Sumerians. Write *Yes* if the statement is suggested in one of the pictures. Write *No* if it is not.**

   a. ___ Sumerians were familiar with the wheel.

   b. ___ Sumerians worked with metal.

   c. ___ Sumerians had small families.

   d. ___ Sumerians worshiped many gods.

CHAPTER 6
Lesson 2 Reading Strategy
The Contributions of the Sumerians

(*A Message of Ancient Days* **pp. 156–161**)

Think About Words   This reading strategy helps you figure out the meaning of new words. When you come to an unfamiliar word, look for word parts you already know and use clues such as context and pictures.

1. **Look at the picture on page 157 and read the caption. Mark an *X* next to the best definition for the word *nomad*.**

   ___ A nomad is a flock of sheep.

   ___ A nomad is a shepherd who moves with the flock when the seasons change.

   ___ A nomad is a person who makes sure that the sheep stay together.

2. **Without using a dictionary, write what you think the word *polytheism* means.**

   _____

   Read the first sentence under "The Sumerian Religion" on page 158. Now write a definition for the word *polytheism*.

   _____

3. **Read the information under "Using Picture Writing" on page 160. Look at the word *pictographs*. What word similar to pictographs do you already know? Then fill in the chart below?**

   _____

   ## What is the meaning of *pictograph*?

picto	**+**	graph	**=**	pictograph
(to paint)		(to write)		_____

4. **Read the first paragraph under "Simplifying the Pictures" on page 161. Give two clues from your reading that help you understand what *cuneiform* is.**

   _____

Lesson 2 Summary
The Contributions of the Sumerians

(*A Message of Ancient Days* pp. 156–161)

Summary also on Audiotape

Thinking Focus: What were the Sumerian contributions in government, religion, and education?

The First Kings

We know from the **epic** *Gilgamesh* that the Sumerians thought of their kings as great heroes. But the earliest Sumerian city-states were ruled by priests, rather than by kings. As the city-states became wealthy, they were raided by **nomads** or by other city-states. Strong military leaders were needed to help defend the cities. Over time, these leaders replaced the priests and became kings. At first, the kings took over many of the priests' duties. Later, kings and priests took on separate tasks. The kings ruled, and the priests worked to please the gods.

[?] What circumstances in Mesopotamia led to the rise of kings?

The Sumerian Religion

Sumerian religion was a kind of **polytheism** in which the gods controlled everything. There were about 3,000 lesser gods and four main gods. Like humans, the gods had emotions and needed sleep and food. But unlike humans, they were immortal and all powerful.

Sumerians believed that by pleasing the gods, they could be safe and have good fortune. They pleased the gods through work, prayer, and offerings of food and animals. Many Sumerian artisans created religious art to please the gods. This art has helped archaeologists learn about Sumerian life.

[?] Describe the Sumerians' religion and explain its important role in the lives of the people.

epic
(ĕp' ĭk)
a long poem that tells the story of a hero

nomad
(nŏ' măd')
person who moves with the flocks and herds to find water and pasture

polytheism
(pŏl' ĕ-thē-ĭz' əm)
belief in more than one god

Summary continues on next page

The People of Sumer

Three social classes lived in Sumer. These classes were:

- the king, government officials, important priests, and wealthy merchants and landowners
- farmers, fishers, and artisans
- slaves

Sumer has some of the first records of slavery. Slaves were prisoners from wars, people who didn't own land, people without food or shelter, or children who were sold into slavery. Slaves did have certain rights. They could work in a business, borrow money, and buy their freedom. If a slave and a free person married, their children would be born free.

? What were the three social classes in Sumerian cities and how did they differ?

The Beginnings of Writing

The Sumerians were the first people to keep written records. They invented writing because merchants and traders needed to keep track of their sales. The Sumerians' first written symbols were **pictographs** of traded items. Later, the pictures stood for syllables that formed words. By 2500 B.C., writers simplified the pictures into the wedge-shaped writing known as **cuneiform**. Few people could read and write, however, so they employed **scribes** to read and write messages. Then the Phoenicians invented a simpler way to keep records. Their writing system had 22 symbols in which each symbol stood for one sound. We call this system the alphabet.

? Describe the important steps in the invention of writing, including pictographs, cuneiform, and the alphabet.

pictograph
(pĭk′tə-grăf′)
a picture that stands for a word or idea

cuneiform
(kyōo′nē-ə-fôrm′)
wedge-shaped characters used in writing several ancient languages

scribe
(skrīb)
a professional writer or record keeper

CHAPTER 6

Lesson 3 Preview
The First Empires

(A Message of Ancient Days **pp. 168–173)**

Nations to Empires

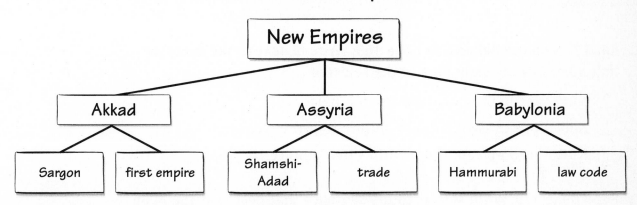

1. **Three empires are named in the graphic. What are they?**

_____

Use words and ideas from the graphic overview to complete the following sentences.

a. King Sargon created the world's first _____.

b. The ruler Shamshi-Adad used _____ to hold his empire together.

c. The Babylonian ruler, _____, is remembered for his law code.

2. **Read the selections from the Code of Hammurabi on page 172. Then read the following statements. Write *Yes* if the statement is suggested in the selections; write *No* if the statement is not suggested in the selections.**

a. ___ Agricultural animals were important in Mesopotamia.

b. ___ Personal property was valued in Mesopotamia.

c. ___ Personal injury was a punishable offense in Mesopotamia.

d. ___ Houses were well cared for in Mesopotamia.

CHAPTER 6

Lesson 3 Reading Strategy
The First Empires

(A Message of Ancient Days pp. 168–173)

Finding the Main Idea   This reading strategy helps you organize and remember what you read. When you finish a selection, jot down the main idea and its supporting details.

1. **Read "Sargon of Akkad" on page 169. Write *M* next to the sentence that best tells the main idea of the selection.**

   ____ King Sargon did not grow up in a palace.

   ____ Rebellions caused Sargon's empire to grow weaker.

   ____ King Sargon created the world's first empire.

2. **Read page 170. Write *M* next to the sentence that best tells the main idea on this page. Write *D* next to the sentences that are supporting details.**

   ____ The Babylonian ruler, Hammurabi, took over Assyrian lands and ruled all of Mesopotamia.

   ____ Power in Mesopotamia shifted to two centers: Assyria in the north and Babylonia in the south.

   ____ Assyria reached its peak of power under the ruler Shamshi-Adad.

3. **Read "The Code of Hammurabi" on pages 172 and 173. Write the main idea and three supporting details in the chart below. (*Hint:* You'll find the main idea in the last paragraph of the section.)**

Main Idea	Supporting Details

Lesson 3 Summary
The First Empires

(*A Message of Ancient Days* pp. 168–173)

Thinking Focus: How did three great rulers build and maintain empires in Mesopotamia?

Sargon of Akkad

Sargon created the world's first **empire**. Sargon's parents were probably herders. They spoke a language called Akkadian. Sargon became a servant of the king of Kish. Historians believe he later killed the king to take the throne.

Once he was king, Sargon built a powerful army. He also founded a capital city, called Akkad, on the Euphrates River. The city-states of Sumer were independent, each with their own ruler. But Akkad conquered them and made them into one kingdom. He later conquered northern Mesopotamia. In time, his empire reached as far east as modern Iran and as far west as the Mediterranean Sea. It might have even reached to Egypt.

empire
(ĕm' pīr')
a nation and other nations it has conquered

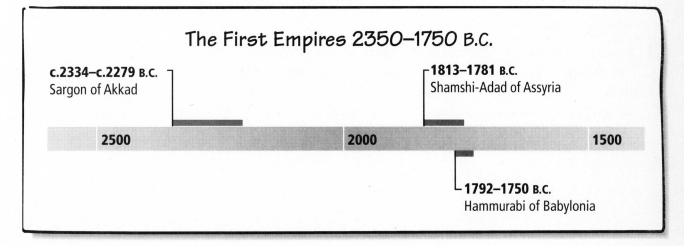

The First Empires 2350–1750 B.C.

c.2334–c.2279 B.C.
Sargon of Akkad

1813–1781 B.C.
Shamshi-Adad of Assyria

2500   2000   1500

1792–1750 B.C.
Hammurabi of Babylonia

Summary continues on next page

After Sargon's death, his son and grandson ruled Sargon's empire. But as the years passed, the empire grew weak. City-states struggled to regain independence. Enemies invaded the empire. Around 2250 B.C., the Gutians from the neighboring Zagros Mountains invaded Akkad and Sargon's empire collapsed.

? What important change did Sargon make in the way Mesopotamia was governed?

Rival Empires

Power in Mesopotamia shifted to two new centers: Assyria in the north and Babylonia in the south. Assyria reached its peak of power under the rule of Shamshi-Adad. Like Sargon, Shamshi-Adad was a great conqueror. He held his empire together through both trade and force. He also had his sons rule parts of his rich kingdom. But Shamshi-Adad and his sons never felt safe. They particularly worried about neighboring Babylonia.

A young Babylonian leader named Hammurabi was gaining power during the last years of Shamshi-Adad's life. As Hammurabi began to extend his rule, he conquered Assyria. He later conquered all of Mesopotamia. Hammurabi sent governors, judges, tax collectors, and military commanders to all parts of his empire to help him maintain a strong central government. One of his greatest achievements was writing an organized set of laws called the **Code** of Hammurabi. His code helped people live responsible, lawful lives.

? Support this statement: Although their empires did not survive long after they died, in many ways Shamshi-Adad and Hammurabi were capable rulers.

code
(kōd)

an organized set of laws or rules

CHAPTER 6

Lesson 4 Preview
New Empires

(*A Message of Ancient Days* pp. 175–180)

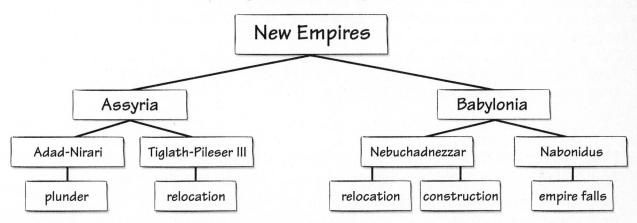

Assyria and Babylonia

1. **The graphic overview gives information about two new Mesopotamian empires.**

   a. What were the names of the two new empires?

   _____

   _____

   b. The graphic overview shows the rulers of the two new empires.
      Name these rulers.

   _____

   _____

2. **Look at the map on page 176.**

   a. Use the map key to help you tell which of the two new empires
      was larger.

   _____

   _____

   b. What bodies of water did Babylonia control?

   _____

   _____

CHAPTER 6

Lesson 4 Reading Strategy
New Empires

(*A Message of Ancient Days* pp. 175–180)

Compare and Contrast   This reading strategy helps you understand how events are similar and different. As you read about historical events, think about how they compare and contrast with events you already know.

1. Read the red subheadings on page 176 and 177. What two empires are compared and contrasted in this lesson?

    _____

2. Read the statements in the chart below. Then read about the New Assyrian and New Babylonian empires on pages 176–180. Use the chart to compare and contrast the two empires by writing *Yes* or *No* after each statement.

Compare and Contrast	New Assyrian Empire	New Babylonian Empire
a. showed mercy to conquered people		
b. relocated rebels		
c. built buildings		

3. Look at the photographs on pages 177 and 179. Write several sentences comparing and contrasting the artistic skill of the Assyrians and the Babylonians.

    _____

    _____

    _____

    _____

    _____

Lesson 4 Summary
New Empires

(A Message of Ancient Days pp. 175–180)

Thinking Focus: How were the New Assyrian and New Babylonian empires alike, and how were they different?

A New Assyrian Empire

In the late 900s B.C., the Assyrians came to power once again. Their well-equipped army showed no mercy for the people it conquered. The army murdered, tortured, and enslaved its enemies. It stole the wealth of conquered cities in order to build its own great cities. To end rebellions, King Tiglath-Pileser III moved rebels to faraway parts of the empire.

The conquered people never gave their loyalty to the hated Assyrians. Neighboring armies built up strength. Then they joined together to defeat the Assyrians in 612 B.C. Power once again swung to the south.

? What policies of the Assyrian rulers helped to cause the eventual downfall of their empire?

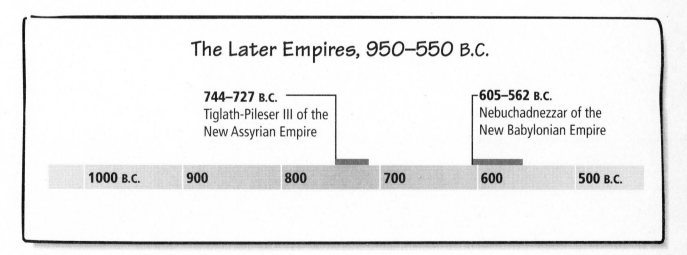

The Later Empires, 950–550 B.C.

744–727 B.C.
Tiglath-Pileser III of the
New Assyrian Empire

605–562 B.C.
Nebuchadnezzar of the
New Babylonian Empire

1000 B.C.   900   800   700   600   500 B.C.

*Summary continues
on next page*

A New Babylonian Empire

The Babylonians of the New Babylonian Empire were great conquerors and traders. King Nebuchadnezzar used the wealth from conquests to build great city walls, temples, and hanging gardens. He also rebuilt Babylon's magnificent ziggurat, or temple tower.

Science flourished during this time. **Astronomers** developed calendars. The hour was divided into 60 minutes. Place value was introduced into mathematics.

But conquered peoples were no better off under the Babylonians than they had been under the Assyrians. To put down rebellions, Nebuchadnezzar sent thousands of people into **exile.** Under King Nabonidus, the people suffered with taxes, famine, and civil war. When a foreign invader, Cyrus the Great, came to conquer Babylonia, the people welcomed him.

? Why were the Babylonians finally unable to maintain their empire?

astronomer
(ə-strŏn′ə-mər)

a scientist who observes and studies the moon, planets, and stars

exile
(ĕg′zīl)

forced removal from one's own country

Chapter Overview
Ancient Egypt

Fill in the blank spaces below with information from the chapter.

When:
4000 B.C.–A.D. 350
Where:
Egypt and Nubia
Who:
Egyptians, Kushites

Egypt and Nubia

Geography

_____ River   Desert

Society

religion   social classes   _____ writing

History

Old Kingdom   New Kingdom   Kush at _____

_____ Kingdom   Kush at Napata

CHAPTER 7

Lesson 1 Preview
The Gift of the Nile

(*A Message of Ancient Days* pp. 186–190)

Regions in Ancient Egypt		
	Upper Egypt	**Lower Egypt**
Symbol	white crown	red crown
Landform	long, narrow river valley	shorter, triangle shaped delta
	Nile	**Sahara**
Egyptian name	Black land	Red land
Kind of soil	moist, fertile river valley	dry, barren desert

1. **Look at the graphic overview. Then complete each sentence below.**

   a. The symbol of Lower Egypt was the _____.

   b. The symbol of Upper Egypt was the _____.

   c. The soil along the Nile was _____.

   d. The soil in the Sahara was _____.

2. **Find the Nile River on the map on page 187 of your text. Then look at the photograph on page 186.**

   a. Which part of the photograph does the green area of the map stand for?

   _____

   b. What part does the yellow area stand for?

   _____

CHAPTER 7

Lesson 1 Reading Strategy
The Gift of the Nile

(*A Message of Ancient Days* pp. 186–190)

Using the Visuals   This reading strategy helps you use photographs, maps, charts, and illustrations to help you understand what you read. As you read, be sure to study the visuals and carefully read the captions.

1. **Look at the map of Egypt on page 187 and the photograph on page 186. Use what you see in both visuals to draw a conclusion about Egypt's natural boundaries. Check the statement that most closely matches your conclusion.**

    ___ It would be easy for invaders to cross the desert and shoot down at the ancient Egyptians.

    ___ Invaders who sailed up the Nile would probably not be stopped by natural boundaries or Egyptian soldiers.

    ___ Most invaders would have to come across the sea or the desert, where they could be easily seen.

2. **Study the visual about making paper on page 189. Write a short title for each picture in the diagram.**

    Step One: _____

    Step Two: _____

    Step Three: _____

    Step Four: _____

    Step Five: _____

3. **What can you learn about the history of ancient Egypt by studying the picture of the double crown on page 190?**

    _____

    _____

Lesson 1 Summary
The Gift of the Nile

(*A Message of Ancient Days* pp. 186–190)

Thinking Focus: What did the ancient Egyptians accomplish because of the "gifts of the Nile"?

The Geography of the Nile

The Nile flows north from East Africa to the Mediterranean Sea. Along the way there are rough, rocky areas called **cataracts**. Near the Mediterranean, the river turns into a fertile **delta**. Egypt's natural boundaries—mountains, deserts, and the Mediterranean Sea—protected ancient Egypt from invaders.

cataract
(kăt′ə-răkt′)
the steep rapids in a river; a large waterfall

delta
(dĕl′tə)
a triangle-shaped area of rich soil near the mouth of a river

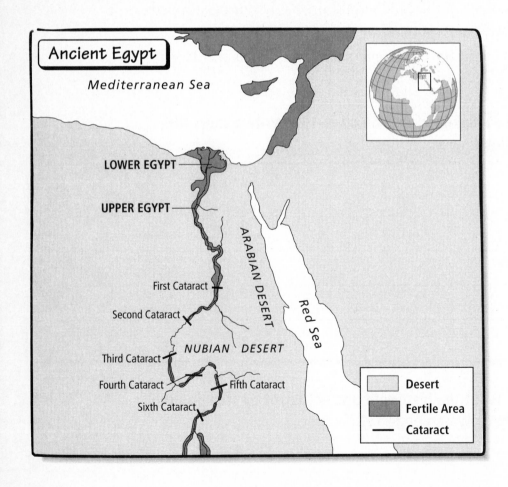

Ancient Egypt

Mediterranean Sea

LOWER EGYPT

UPPER EGYPT

ARABIAN DESERT

Red Sea

First Cataract

Second Cataract

NUBIAN DESERT

Third Cataract

Fourth Cataract — Fifth Cataract

Sixth Cataract

Desert
Fertile Area
Cataract

Summary continues on next page

Reading Support Resources

Away from the Nile, the land of Egypt is dry desert. So the lives of the Egyptians depended on the Nile. Here are some of the "gifts" that the Nile gave the ancient Egyptians:

- Seasonal floods watered the farmers' fields. Farmers also built dams and irrigation systems to take advantage of the floods.

- The Nile left behind thick, black mud when it flooded. This dark mud made the soil very fertile.

- Egyptians ate fish from the Nile and ducks, geese, and other birds that lived in the nearby marshes.

- They used **papyrus** reeds that grew along the Nile's banks to make baskets, boats, sandals, and paper.

[?] Explain how water, mud, plants, and animals were all "gifts of the Nile" to the Egyptians.

papyrus
(pə-pī′rəs)

a long, thin reed used to make writing material and other things

dynasty
(dī′nə-stē)

a series of rulers from the same family

The Union of Two Lands

Ancient Egypt had two parts. Upper Egypt was the southern part. Lower Egypt was the northern part. Each part had a king. Legend says that King Menes of Upper Egypt defeated Lower Egypt in about 3100 B.C. King Menes started the first Egyptian **dynasty.**

The history of ancient Egypt is divided into three periods:

- Old Kingdom (2686 to 2181 B.C.)
- Middle Kingdom (2055 to 1650 B.C.)
- New Kingdom (1570 to 1070 B.C.)

During the Old Kingdom, the Egyptians built the pyramids. During the Middle Kingdom, they created great literature, art, and architecture. During the New Kingdom, they built an empire. But even before the Old Kingdom, the Egyptians had accomplished many things. They had irrigated their fields, formed governments, invented hieroglyphic writing, and created a special system of customs and beliefs.

[?] What were some important early accomplishments of the Egyptians?

CHAPTER 7

Lesson 2 Preview
Life in Ancient Egypt

(A Message of Ancient Days pp. 191–198)*

Daily Life in Egypt

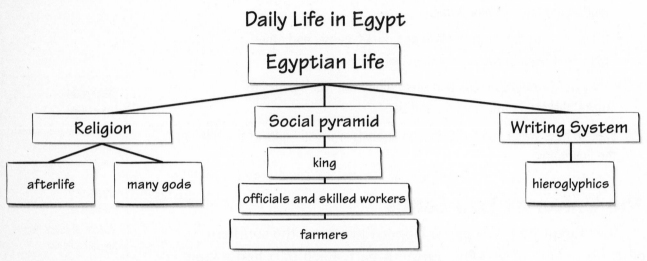

1. **The graphic overview shows ideas and social structures that were important in the everyday life of the ancient Egyptians. Use it to answer the questions. Circle your answers.**

    a. Which word or phrase is connected with the ancient Egyptians' religious beliefs?

farmers	hieroglyphics	afterlife

    b. Which word or phrase is connected with the ancient Egyptians' social structure?

many gods	king	hieroglyphics

    c. Which word or phrase is connected with the ancient Egyptians' means of communication?

hieroglyphics	skilled workers	afterlife

CHAPTER 7

Lesson 2 Reading Strategy
Life in Ancient Egypt

(*A Message of Ancient Days* pp. 191–198)

Predict/Infer This reading strategy helps you understand what you have read and what you will read next. Before you read a section, think about the titles, pictures, and captions. Then think about what will happen in the selection.

1. **Read the main heads and subheads on pages 192 and 193. Then check the statement that you predict will most closely explain the religion of ancient Egyptians.**

   ___ Ancient Egyptians did not believe in life after death. They believed people should spend their lives making sacrifices to their gods.

   ___ Ancient Egyptians believed that after death, their spirits would live on. It was important to worship the gods.

   ___ Ancient Egyptians worshiped one god. They also worshiped dead people whose names were in the *Book of the Dead*.

2. **Read the first two paragraphs of "A Writing System" and then stop. Use the chart to write down what you learned and then make a prediction about what will happen next.**

What I Know	What I Predict

3. **Look at the pictures of the workers on pages 197 and 198. Read the captions. Then make an inference about which worker was of a higher social class.**

   _____

Lesson 2 Summary
Life in Ancient Egypt

(A Message of Ancient Days **pp. 191–198)**

Thinking Focus: Describe the religious ideas and the social structure of the ancient Egyptians.

The Egyptian Religion

The Egyptian religion was based on belief in an **afterlife**. To prepare for the afterlife, the Egyptians built pyramids, or huge tombs. Before a body was placed in a pyramid, it was **embalmed**. Embalming protected the body from decay and changed the body into a **mummy**. Many everyday objects went into the tomb along with the body. Such objects included food and drink, jewelry, games, and sometimes even an embalmed pet. The walls of the tomb were decorated with scenes from the life of the person who had died. A priest would ask the gods to guide the person to the next world. The priest might say hymns, prayers, or read from the *Book of the Dead.*

Egyptians believed in many gods. Some, like Osiris, were linked with death and the afterlife. Some, like Ra and Amon, were creators and rulers of the world. There were gods of music and dancing, love and beauty, healing and learning, and family. Each Egyptian village had its own special god. Ordinary Egyptian homes included shrines to the family's favorite gods.

[?] What religious beliefs account for the pyramids and mummies of ancient Egypt?

A Writing System

Ancient Egyptians invented a kind of picture writing called **hieroglyphics**. Like the cuneiform writing of Mesopotamia, it was very complex and hard for historians to figure out. The key to understanding Egyptian hieroglyphics was a stone slab found near the Egyptian village of Rosetta in 1799. The stone had writing in hieroglyphics and in two other languages. Scholars

afterlife
(ăf'tər-līf')
a life believed to continue after death on earth

embalm
(ĕm-bäm')
to treat a dead body to keep it from decaying

mummy
(mŭm'ē)
the body of a human or animal after it has been embalmed

hieroglyphics
(hī'ər-ə-glĭf'ĭks)
the Egyptian writing system in which picture symbols stand for words or sounds

Summary continues on next page

decoded the hieroglyphics by comparing them to the other languages. Historians could then read the many writings the ancient Egyptians had left behind.

[?] Compare and contrast the writing systems of the Egyptians and the Mesopotamians.

A Social Pyramid

The social system of ancient Egypt was like a pyramid. At the top was the king, who owned all the land and had complete control over the people. Priests and government officials also belonged to the upper levels of society. Artisans and skilled workers made up the next level of society. They included carpenters, painters, jewelers, brick makers, and stonemasons. Farmers formed the base of the Egyptian social pyramid. By raising food, farmers supported all the other levels of Egyptian society. When they were not working in the fields, farmers worked on irrigation systems, pyramids, and temples.

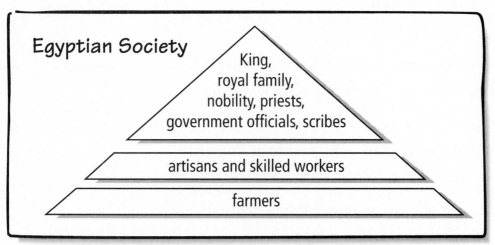

[?] What were the occupations of the people at the top, middle, and bottom of the Egyptian social pyramid?

C H A P T E R   7

Lesson 3 Preview
The New Kingdom

(A Message of Ancient Days **pp. 199–203)**

The Reigns of Hatshepsut and Thutmose III

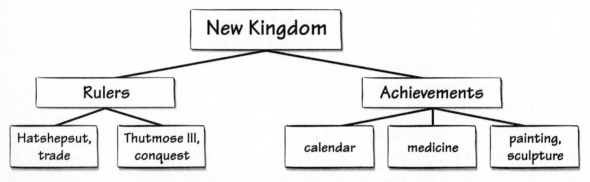

1. **Use the graphic overview above to take notes about things you will want to remember from this lesson.**

   a. Important rulers from the New Kingdom:

   _____

   b. Important accomplishments during the New Kingdom:

   _____

   c. Which Egyptian ruler wanted to improve life at home?

   _____

   d. Which Egyptian ruler wanted to expand the kingdom?

   _____

2. **Look at the picture on page 199 of your text. Read the caption. Name two things that the picture tells about Hatshepsut.**

   _____

   _____

   _____

   _____

CHAPTER 7
Lesson 3 Reading Strategy
The New Kingdom

(*A Message of Ancient Days* pp. 199–203)

Think About Words   This reading strategy helps you figure out the meaning of new words. When you come to an unfamiliar word, look for word parts you already know and use clues such as context and pictures.

1. Read "Hatshepsut's Reign" on page 200. Then look at the photograph on page 201. Read the caption. How does this picture help you understand the meaning of the word *obelisk?*

   _____

2. Sometimes a synonym for an unknown word appears nearby—often in the same sentence. Find a synonym for *erected* in this sentence from page 200:
   Note that Hatshepsut built a great temple and erected obelisks, but she did not build a pyramid.
   Write a synonym for *erected.*

   _____

3. Sometimes new words are defined in the sentence in which they appear. Skim page 202 to find the word *Sirius*. Read the sentence in which it appears. Then write the definition of *Sirius.*

   _____

4. Find the following words on pages 202–203. Complete the chart by writing a definition for each word and any clues you used to write the definition.

WORD	DEFINITION	CLUE
lunar		
interior		
apprenticeship		

Lesson 3 Summary
The New Kingdom

(A Message of Ancient Days pp. 199–203)

Thinking Focus: What were the achievements of the Egyptians during the New Kingdom period?

New Kingdom Rulers

During the New Kingdom, Egyptians began to call their rulers **pharaohs** as a sign of respect. Pharaoh meant "great house." Two great pharaohs of the New Kingdom were Hatshepsut and Thutmose III.

Hatshepsut was the half-sister of Thutmose II. When Thutmose II died, his son was too young to rule. Hatshepsut took over the government in his place, and she continued to rule for 20 years. Hatshepsut was an intelligent and skillful ruler. She sent out trade expeditions that returned with gold, ivory, rare woods, and other valuable items. She also built a great temple and put up **obelisks**.

When Hatshepsut died, her nephew, Thutmose III, became pharaoh. Thutmose III was a successful military leader. He extended the empire from Nubia to the Euphrates River. His victories brought great wealth to Egypt. Under Thutmose III, Egypt became one of the Mediterranean's most powerful kingdoms. Later rulers continued to enlarge his empire.

? Compare and contrast the two strong rulers Hatshepsut and Thutmose III.

pharaoh
(fâr′ō)
a ruler of ancient Egypt

obelisk
(ŏb′ə-lĭsk)
a tall, four-sided stone pillar that rises to a point

Achievements of the Egyptians

The ancient Egyptians were skilled architects, sculptors, and engineers. But they excelled in other areas, too. For example, they created an accurate lunar calendar. The Babylonians had also invented a calendar based on the moon's cycles, but the Egyptian calendar was more accurate. The Egyptians had noticed the cycles of the moon. But they also noticed Sirius, the brightest star in the sky. Sirius disappeared for several months every year.

Summary continues on next page

It always reappeared just when flood season began. By basing their calendar on both the moon and the star Sirius, the Egyptians could measure time in a way that almost exactly matched the seasons.

The world's oldest scientific document was written in Egypt in the early 1500s B.C. The document seems to be a handbook for surgeons. It describes common injuries and illnesses, their symptoms, and their treatment. The writer's attention to detail and the accuracy of his observations were remarkable for that time.

Ancient Egypt is also known for its art. Egyptian artists trained for many years. Their tomb paintings are among the finest achievements of ancient Egypt.

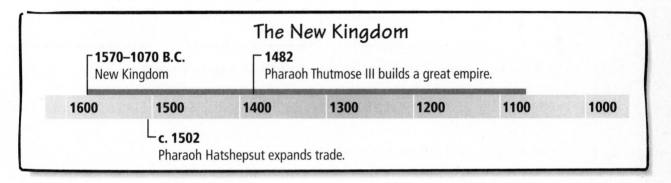

The New Kingdom

- **1570–1070 B.C.** New Kingdom
- **1482** Pharaoh Thutmose III builds a great empire.

| 1600 | 1500 | 1400 | 1300 | 1200 | 1100 | 1000 |

c. 1502 Pharaoh Hatshepsut expands trade.

? What were some important achievements of the Egyptians during the New Kingdom period?

C H A P T E R 7
Lesson 4 Preview
Egypt and the Nubian Kingdom of Kush

(*A Message of Ancient Days* pp. 210–214)

Two Ancient Civilizations

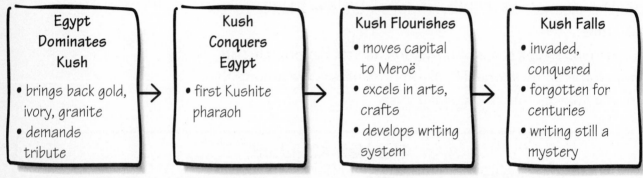

1. **Study the graphic overview. Then number the sentences below from *1* to *4* to show the order in which the events occurred.**

___ Kush conquers Egypt.

___ Kush fell and was forgotten for centuries.

___ Kushite culture flourishes.

___ Egypt dominates Kush.

2. **Look at the picture on page 212, and read the caption. Which statement best explains the idea of the picture?**

___ a. The Kushites dominated Egypt.

___ b. The Egyptians dominated Kush.

___ c. Egypt and Kush were traders.

Lesson 4 Reading Strategy
Egypt and the Nubian Kingdom of Kush

(*A Message of Ancient Days* pp. 210–214)

Sequence This reading strategy helps you follow what is happening in your reading. As you read, pay attention to dates and times, as well as to words such as *before, finally, after,* and *then.*

1. **Read page 211. Then number the following events to show the order in which they happened.**

   ___ Thutmose III demanded tribute.

   ___ Beginning around 2000 B.C., the Egyptians began trading with Nubia.

   ___ Egypt built forts and trading posts in Nubia.

2. **Sometimes dates in the selection tell you the exact sequence. Read "Nubia Conquers Egypt" on page 212. Write a sentence to tell what happened in this year.**

   750 B.C. _____

   _____

   _____

3. **Read these sentences. Underline the word in each sentence that is a clue to sequence.**

   a. Next, Kashta's son Piankhy, defeated the warring princes who controlled the Nile Delta.

   b. Piankhy then went on to complete his conquest of Egypt by taking the rest of Lower Egypt.

   c. His successor, Shabaka, became the first Nubian pharaoh of Egypt.

Lesson 4 Summary
Egypt and the Nubian Kingdom of Kush

(A Message of Ancient Days pp. 210–214)

Thinking Focus: Why is Kush called one of the great civilizations of ancient Africa?

Egypt Dominates Kush

Nubia stretches along the Nile Valley from the first to the fifth cataract. Several kingdoms prospered in Nubia at different times. One of these was the kingdom of Kush. Kush often interacted with its northern neighbor, Egypt. During the Middle Kingdom, the Egyptians built forts in Kush to have **access** to their trade routes—and to Nubian gold and ivory. When Egypt invaded Kush in the late 1400s B.C., Kush began to pay an annual **tribute** of ivory, perfumes, oils, and grains to Egypt. Egypt had a strong influence on the culture of Kush. Kushites came to believe in an afterlife and in the Egyptian gods. Some Kushites learned Egyptian crafts and hieroglyphics.

? How did Kushite society and Egyptian society influence each other?

access
(ăk′sĕs′)
a way to approach or enter a place

tribute
(trĭb′yoŏt)
a gift or payment given to show respect

Kush Conquers Egypt

Kush was part of Egypt until the end of the New Kingdom. Then Egypt began to weaken. The strong pharaohs had died and priests and nobles tried to seize power. The Egyptian kings were not able to keep the Kushites under control. The Kushite ruler Kashta saw a chance to break away from Egypt and to expand his own kingdom. By 750 B.C., Kashta had defeated Upper Egypt. Kashta's son, Piankhy, finished the job by conquering Lower Egypt. Shabaka, who followed Piankhy, became the first Kushite pharaoh of Egypt. His kingdom reached from the Mediterranean Sea to the border of what is now Ethiopia.

? How did the Nubian leaders become Egyptian pharaohs when Egypt was weak?

Summary continues on next page

Reading Support Resources

Kush's Last Thousand Years

Kashta's dynasty lasted less than 100 years. By 654 B.C., Assyria had driven the Kushites from Egypt. But Kushite kings still ruled their former kingdom from their capital of Napata.

In 591 B.C., after being defeated by an Egyptian army, the Kushites moved their capital south to Meroë. The new capital became a center for iron-making, as well as for trade and crafts. Meroë thrived for more than 600 years. During that time, it was governed by several powerful queens. The wealth of the queens' tombs shows the high position these women held.

Egyptian influence gradually decreased. The Kushites invented their own hieroglyphic writing and began to worship a new god. Then, in A.D. 350, the ruler of Axum, a neighboring kingdom, invaded Meroë and burned it to the ground.

For centuries, Meroë was forgotten. Archaeologists have now explored the ruins of Meroë and other Kushite cities. They have learned much about this great civilization, but much more is still unknown.

? What happened to the Egyptian influence in Kush in the centuries after the Assyrian conquest?

Chapter Overview
Ancient India

Fill in the blank spaces below with information from the chapter.

When:
2500 B.C.– A.D. 467
Where: Indus Valley and India
Who: Hindus, Buddhists

The Beginning of Hinduism and Buddhism

The _____ Valley Civilization

Aryans

Vedic Religion

Life of the Buddha

Teachings of Buddhism

Rule of Asoka

Golden Age of Hinduism

epic _____

_____ Empire

CHAPTER 8

Lesson 1 Preview
The Indus Valley Civilization

(*A Message of Ancient Days* pp. 222–228)

Factors That Led to Civilization in the Indus Valley

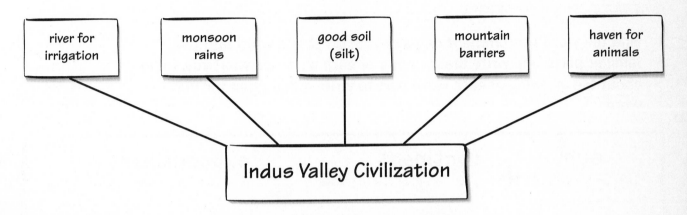

1. **Look at the graphic overview. List five factors that led to the development of civilization in the Indus River Valley. Put a star next to the factors that you think may relate to the Indus River itself.**

   a. _____

   b. _____

   c. _____

   d. _____

   e. _____

2. **Look at the map on page 223 of your text. What mountain ranges separate India from the rest of Asia?**

   _____

CHAPTER 8
Lesson 1 Reading Strategy
The Indus Valley Civilization
(A Message of Ancient Days **pp. 220–228)**

Think About Words This reading strategy helps you figure out the meaning of new words. When you come to an unfamiliar word, look for word parts you already know and use clues such as context and pictures.

1. Find the word *subcontinent* on page 223. Break the word into two familiar parts, and write the meaning of each part. Use what you know about the meaning of each word part to write a definition for the word.

sub + continent = subcontinent

_____   _____   _____

2. Look at the map and photo on page 224. Use what you see to tell what kind of landform the Himalayas are.

_____

_____

3. A definition or related word that appears near an unknown word may help you define the unknown word. Find *silt* on page 224. Read the sentence in which *silt* appears. What definition is given for *silt*?

_____

_____

4. Read the last paragraph before "The Great River Civilization" on page 225. Find the word *stable. Stable* can have several different meanings. Use context to determine the meaning of *stable* on this page. Write the clue that helped you determine the meaning.

_____

_____

_____

Lesson 1 Summary
The Indus Valley Civilization

(A Message of Ancient Days pp. 222–228)

Thinking Focus: What evidence have archaeologists found of a highly developed civilization in the Indus River Valley?

Almost a Continent

Huge mountain ranges separate the **subcontinent** of India from the rest of Asia. These mountains are the source of major rivers. One of these rivers is the Indus River. The Indus Valley was an ideal place for people to settle. The river provided people with water routes for trade. The Indus also flooded often in ancient times. It left behind rich **silt** that made the land ideal for farming. Monsoons regularly brought a period of rain. So farmers knew just when to plant. Crops such as wheat and barley grew well. In ancient times, animals also roamed the plains of the Indus Valley. The stable food supply brought settlers, who began to build cities.

subcontinent
(sŭb′kŏn′tə-nənt)
a large land area that is part of a continent but is separated from it in some way

silt
(sĭlt)
a fine-grained soil often left behind on riverbanks after floods

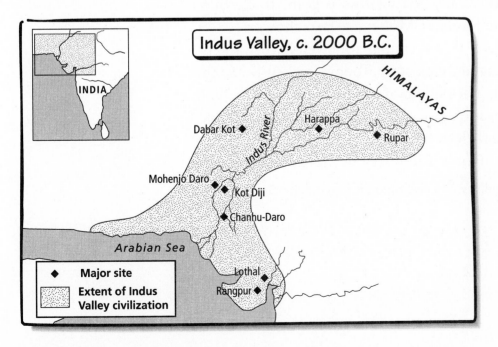

Indus Valley, c. 2000 B.C.

INDIA

HIMALAYAS

Dabar Kot
Harappa
Rupar
Indus River
Mohenjo Daro
Kot Diji
Chanhu-Daro

Arabian Sea

Lothal
Rangpur

♦ Major site
Extent of Indus Valley civilization

? How did the geographical location of the Indus Valley make possible the growth of a civilization there?

Summary continues on next page

The Great River Civilization

The civilization in the Indus Valley included Mohenjo-Daro, Harappa, and more than 70 other sites. No written records that modern historians can read have been found. But archaeologists have made important discoveries. All the towns were built on a similar plan by workers who were skillful. Historians believe that there must have been a central government to make the plans and see that they were carried out.

We also know that the Indus Valley people traded with other cultures. Written records from Mesopotamia mention trade between the Indus Valley and Sumer. Products from the Indus Valley—such as stone beads and seals—have been found in Mesopotamia and near the Persian Gulf. Archeologists have also discovered merchants' stone weights and trademarks throughout the Indus Valley.

[?] What products did the Indus Valley cities export, and how do we know?

Echoes from Abandoned Cities

The Indus Valley civilization lasted 1,000 years. No one knows why it finally declined. Archaeologists have found skeletons of people huddled together, so perhaps a natural disaster occurred.

Even though the Indus Valley civilization is gone, traces of its culture remain. A statue found at Mohenjo-Daro shows a woman wearing a bracelet that is similar to jewelry worn today by many women in India and Pakistan. Today chicken is a staple food all over the world. The people of the Indus Valley first had the idea to raise chickens for food. The Indus people had learned to spin and weave cotton cloth by 2000 B.C. Today making cotton cloth is still an important industry in India.

[?] What evidence of the Indus Valley civilization is found in modern India?

CHAPTER 8

Lesson 2 Preview
Arrival of the Aryans

(*A Message of Ancient Days* pp. 229–234)

The Beginnings of Indian Culture

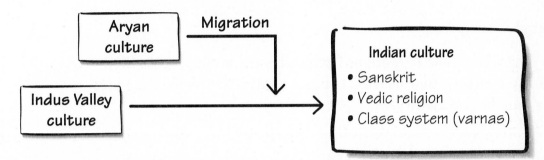

1. **The graphic overview tells the story of the beginning of Indian Culture. Use it to complete the sentences below.**

   a. The people who were in the area first were part of the

   _____ culture.

   b. The people who may have migrated to the area were from the

   _____ culture.

   c. Together, they created a culture with these important aspects:

   _____

   _____

   _____

2. **Look through the illustrations in the lesson to find a tool the Aryan people contributed to the culture.**

   a. What page does the tool appear on?

   _____

   b. How was the tool used?

   _____

   _____

CHAPTER 8

Lesson 2 Reading Strategy
Arrival of the Aryans

(A Message of Ancient Days **pp. 229–234)**

Compare and Contrast This reading strategy helps you understand how events are similar and different. As you read about historical events, think about how they compare and contrast with events you already know.

1. **Read "Indo-European Migrations," which begins on page 229. Then check the sentence that best describes a contrast between the Indus Valley people and the Aryans.**

   ___ The Indus Valley people lived in the river valley, while the Aryans may have migrated to the area.

   ___ The Aryans may have come to the Indus River Valley through treacherous mountain passes.

   ___ Both the Indus Valley people and the Aryans lived together.

2. **Read "Social Classes" on page 233. Then check the sentence that describes a contrast between two social classes.**

   ___ The most powerful class was made up of priests, but the lowest class was made up of servants.

   ___ The four social classes are described in the Vedas.

   ___ The highest and lowest classes both helped the community.

3. **Read "What Remains Today of Aryan Ways?" on page 234. Use the chart to compare three things from the Aryan past with India today.**

India Then	India Now

Lesson 2 Summary
Arrival of the Aryans

(*A Message of Ancient Days* pp. 229–234)

Thinking Focus: What did the Aryans contribute to Indian culture?

From Where Did the Aryans Come?

As Indus River Valley civilization was coming to an end, a new group of people began to take over the Indus Valley. They were the **Aryan** people. The Aryans spoke a language called *Sanskrit*. Historians disagree about where the Aryans came from. Some think that Aryan culture grew out of the Indus Valley civilization. Others think that the Aryans were a separate culture and that they moved into the Indus Valley a few people at a time.

According to the separate-culture theory, the Aryans were part of a large group now called Indo-Europeans. They lived in the grasslands of Eastern Europe and traveled from place to place herding cattle, goats, and sheep. They also tamed horses and built chariots that allowed them to move around freely and to fight more effectively than soldiers on foot.

Around 2000 B.C., groups of Indo-Europeans began a **migration** from their homeland. Some groups moved west and south. The Aryans moved east toward India.

Early Aryans passed along their beliefs orally. Priests had the job of memorizing a long collection of sacred poems and hymns called the Vedas. In this way, they handed down their traditions from generation to generation.

[?] What advantages enabled the Aryans to successfully take over the Indus Valley?

Aryan
(âr′ē-ən)

a seminomad who came originally from Eastern Europe and spoke an Indo-European language

migration
(mī-grā′shən)

permanent movement of people from one region to settle in another

*Summary continues
on next page*

What Do the Vedas Reveal?

We know about Aryan life through the Vedas. According to the Vedas, the universe is divided into three regions—earth, atmosphere, and sky. Gods occupy each region and control the forces of nature. For example, Indra, the god of war, is the keeper of cosmic order in the world. Aryan priests performed religious ceremonies to keep the universe in harmony. The most important ceremony was the fire sacrifice, at which food and sometimes animals were burned.

Aryan society had four classes. These classes were:

- priests;
- rajas (rulers) and warriors;
- merchants and peasants; and
- servants.

> **caste**
> (kăst)
> a division within India's social class system

In time, these classes developed subgroups, called **castes**, based on specific jobs. A person's caste was permanent. It determined the person's job, daily activities, and marriage partner.

[?] What do the Vedas reveal about Aryan society and religion?

What Remains Today of Aryan Ways?

Aryan culture spread throughout the region as Aryan groups settled down and established kingdoms. They raised cattle. They also made iron and used iron axes and plows. With these tools, they cleared farmland and grew crops. They learned to weave and dye cloth and to make jewelry and pottery.

Many things in modern India began with the Aryans. Hindi, a language of India, has roots in the Aryan language. Castes, too, are a part of Indian life. But the Aryans' most lasting contribution is religion. People still study the Vedas today.

[?] What evidence of the Aryan tradition is found in modern India?

CHAPTER 8
Lesson 3 Preview
Beginning of Buddhism

(*A Message of Ancient Days* pp. 235–240)

The Roots of Buddhism

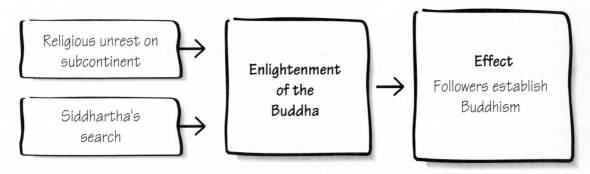

1. **Study the graphic overview. Then look at each pair of events below. Circle the event in each pair that happened first.**

   a. Establishment of Buddhism   Religious unrest

   b. Siddhartha's search   Enlightenment of the Buddha

   c. Enlightenment of the Buddha   Establishment of Buddhism

2. **Read the comic strip on page 236. Then complete the following sentences:**

   a. As he was riding in his chariot, Siddhartha saw a

   _____.

   b. Siddhartha went in search of _____.

CHAPTER 8
Lesson 3 Reading Strategy
Beginning of Buddhism

(*A Message of Ancient Days* pp. 235–240)

Summarize This reading strategy helps you remember key points about what you have read. When you get to a good break in your reading, stop and write down the main ideas of what you have read.

1. **Read "The Peaceful Road" on page 237. Check the sentence that best summarizes the Buddha's life after his enlightenment.**

   ___ Buddha spoke to five followers in a park near Sarnath.

   ___ Buddha traveled and taught Buddhist dharma.

   ___ The Buddha died at the age of 80.

2. **Read "The Middle Way" on page 237. Check the sentence that best summarizes the Buddha's attitude toward earthly possessions.**

   ___ Greed for possessions is not against Buddhist dharma.

   ___ The Buddha's followers were encouraged to give up all their possessions.

   ___ The Buddha's followers should follow a policy of moderation.

3. **Read "A Great Buddhist Ruler" on page 229. Write one sentence to summarize how Asoka's conversion to Buddhism changed his way of ruling.**

   _____

   _____

   _____

Summary also on
Audiotape

Lesson 3 Summary
Beginning of Buddhism

(*A Message of Ancient Days* pp. 235–240)

Thinking Focus: What are the main teachings of Buddhism?

Life of the Buddha

Buddhism is one of the world's major religions. It was started by Siddhartha Gautama, who lived on the Indian subcontinent from about 563 to 483 B.C.

During Siddhartha's lifetime, India was in a period of religious unrest. People had begun to doubt the need for the priests' Vedic rituals. According to legend, one day Siddhartha gave up all his possessions except for a robe and a rice bowl. He traveled about, seeking answers to spiritual questions. But he was not satisfied with the answers given by religious leaders of the time. He decided to look within himself. Sitting under a tree, Siddhartha meditated for 49 days. His meditations led him to believe that he had found a way to escape suffering. He became known as the Buddha, which means "enlightened one." Enlightenment is what Buddhists called the height of understanding. The Buddha spent the rest of his life teaching the Buddha *dharma,* or law.

[?] What events do Buddhists believe led to Siddhartha's enlightenment?

Teachings of Buddhism

The Buddha taught that all people are equal. He opposed animal sacrifices, and he believed that people could find peace on their own. The Buddha stressed **moderation**—not too much or too little of anything. He explained suffering in his Four Noble Truths. He also preached an Eightfold Path that leads to enlightenment. Steps on the Eightfold Path include acting in a way that does not harm others.

Buddhism
(bōō'dĭz'əm)

a religion that stresses moderation and nonviolence

moderation
(mŏd'ə-rā'shən)

not too much or too little of anything

Summary continues on next page

Buddhists believe in **rebirth**. A person's good or bad deeds travel with him or her into the next life. Meditation is an important part of Buddhism. Meditation calms the mind and allows a person to let go of desires and possessions.

rebirth
(rē-bûrth′)

the belief in a new birth and life set in motion by a person's karma

---

The Four Noble Truths

1. People experience suffering and sorrow.

2. Suffering and sorrow are caused by people's greed, hatred, and ignorance.

3. We can be freed from suffering by overcoming its cause.

4. People can overcome their greed, hatred, and ignorance by practicing the Eightfold Path. This path gives eight steps for living a correct, or right, life.

[?] What is the Eightfold Path, and where does it lead?

A Great Buddhist Ruler

The emperor Asoka was a faithful Buddhist who sent missionaries to lands beyond India. In this way, he started the spread of Buddhism throughout Asia. Asoka belonged to a line of kings known as the Mauryas. The Mauryas built the first great Indian empire. Asoka cared about the happiness and welfare of his people. He also believed in nonviolence and forbade harming animals or people. After Asoka's death the Mauryan empire broke apart into small warring kingdoms.

[?] How did Asoka's Buddhist beliefs influence his rule?

CHAPTER 8

Lesson 4 Preview
The Golden Age

(A Message of Ancient Days pp. 244–50)*

Hindu Life

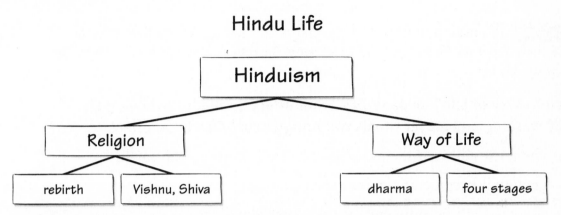

1. The graphic overview shows that Hinduism has two parts that are linked together—religion and way of life. Read the list of words below. Write *R* beside each word that refers to the Hindu religion. Write *L* beside each word that refers to the Hindu way of life.

___ dharma

___ Vishnu, Shiva

___ rebirth

___ four stages

2. Look through the pictures in the lesson, and read the captions. Circle the sentence that describes what the pictures tell you about Hinduism.

   a. Hindu art portrays scenes from the lives of gods and goddesses.

   b. Only male gods are pictured in Hindu art.

CHAPTER 8

Lesson 4 Reading Strategy
The Golden Age

(*A Message of Ancient Days* pp. 244–250)

Cause and Effect   This reading strategy helps you understand events and why they occur. As you read, think about the factors that caused an event. Then think about what the effects of that event may be.

1. **Read "A Way of Life" on page 245. What effect do Hindus believe their daily washing and prayer rituals will bring about? Check the effect.**

   ___ The gods will visit their home when they walk on the earth.

   ___ They will become as clean as their gods.

   ___ Holiness will become part of their everyday lives.

2. **Read "Karma and Rebirth" on page 246. Then complete the sentence below:**

   If a person has good karma in this life, the effect will be _____

   _____

3. **Read "Life's Stages" on page 246. Then complete this sentence:**

   In order to enter the fourth stage, a man or woman must _____

   _____

4. **Complete the chart by writing a cause or an effect for each empty square.**

Causes	Effects
Page 249 Prices and wages needed to be set for each group of merchants.	
Pages 249–250 Mathematicians in ancient India were encouraged to study and create.	
Page 250	The Gupta Empire fell.

Lesson 4 Summary
The Golden Age

(A Message of Ancient Days pp. 244–250)

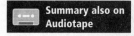
Summary also on Audiotape

Thinking Focus: What are some of the main features of Hinduism?

Beliefs of Hinduism

The roots of **Hinduism** are in the Vedic religion of the Aryans. But Hinduism is not just a religion. It is also a way of life. Every day, Hindus follow washing and prayer rituals, as well as rules about the foods they may eat. Every Hindu home also has a place for meditation.

Hinduism continued the caste system of the Aryans. Another important Hindu idea is *dharma,* or social duties. Dharma also means living in an unselfish way. Like Buddhism, Hinduism stresses *karma* and rebirth. Karma determines what form a person will take in the next lifetime. A Hindu's goal is to reach a state in which rebirth no longer takes place and the person is one with Brahman, or God.

Hindu males in the three upper classes may study the sacred Vedas. When they begin their study, their lives are divided into four stages.

Hinduism
(hĭn'dōō-ĭz'əm)
the major religion and way of life in modern India

- In stage one, they study with a guru, or spiritual teacher.
- In stage two, they marry and raise families. Women, too, have religious duties in the home.
- In stage three, some men and women give up their possessions and meditate.
- In stage four, a few men and women give up everything, including their caste, to become holy persons.

? In what ways is Hinduism a way of life?

Summary continues on next page

The Gupta Empire

Between A.D. 320 and 467, a group of rulers called the Guptas brought a Golden Age to India. India's borders expanded, and trade increased. Elephants and ox-drawn carts carried goods on overland trails, and cargo ships sailed the seas.

India was in a good location for trade. To the west were Rome and the rest of the Mediterranean region, as well as Africa. To the east were China, Southeast Asia, and Indonesia. The Guptas exported luxury goods such as gems, pearls, perfumes, spices, cotton cloth, red dye, and timber. They imported gold from Rome, silk from China, and horses from Saudi Arabia and Central Asia.

Along with increased trade came the growth of **guilds**. Organized according to crafts and trades, the guilds set prices and wages. They also kept watch over the quality of work and the welfare of the workers.

? Where did trade routes lead during Gupta times, and what was traded?

Achievements of Ancient India

Among the achievements of the Guptas are two **epics**, the *Mahabharata* and the *Ramayana*. These epics had been passed down orally through many generations. During the Gupta period, they were written down.

The Guptas also excelled in science, math, and engineering. The astronomer Aryabhata described the earth as a sphere that revolved around the sun. He also calculated the solar year as 365 days. Indian mathematicians devised a number system with nine digits, the zero, and the decimal—a system still in use today.

By A.D. 467, India's Golden Age was coming to an end. Invasions by the White Huns from Central Asia weakened the Gupta empire. Once again, India broke up into small kingdoms.

? Explain some of the achievements of the Gupta period.

guild
(gĭld)

an association of merchants or artisans who do the same type of work

epic
(ĕp′ĭk)

a long poem that tells the story of a hero

Chapter Overview
Ancient China

Fill in the blank spaces below with information from the chapter.

When:
10,000 B.C.–A.D. 220

Who:
Chinese

China: Divided and United

Divided by Land

Great Deserts   High _____

Divided by Belief Systems

Confucianism   Moism   _____   Daoism

United by Early Dynasties

_____   Zhou   Qin   _____

United by Rivers

Transportation   Trade

CHAPTER 9
Lesson 1 Preview
China's Early History

(*A Message of Ancient Days* pp. 262–269)

Five Cultures of Ancient China					
	Prehistory			Early Dynasties	
Culture	Yang shao	Lungshan	Xia	Shang Dynasty	Zhou Dynasty
Era	Neolithic	Neolithic	late Neolithic	Bronze Age	Bronze Age
Major contribution	agriculture	silk	leaders	bronze	picture writing
Religion	many gods	many gods	many gods	ancestor worship oracle bones	Tian, mandate of heaven

1. **Look at the graphic overview. What four features of ancient Chinese cultures can you compare and contrast, using this overview?**

   a. _____

   b. _____

   c. _____

   d. _____

2. **Look at the photos on page 262 and the map on page 263 of your text. Then read the sentences below. If a sentence is true, write *T*. If it is false, write *F*.**

   a. China has high mountains and fertile valleys. ___

   b. China has no mountains that rise over 10,000 feet. ___

   c. Part of China borders on the sea. ___

   d. The deserts of China are along the coast. ___

   e. China has long rivers. ___

CHAPTER 9
Lesson 1 Reading Strategy
China's Early History

(A Message of Ancient Days pp. 262–269)

Summarize This reading strategy helps you remember key points about what you have read. When you get to a good break in your reading, stop and write down the main ideas of what you have read.

1. **Read "China's Geography" on pages 263 and 264. Which of the following is the best summary for this section? Check your answer.**

   ___ Mountains and deserts divided and kept China isolated for thousand of years, but rivers helped link areas within the country.

   ___ Two of China's major rivers are the Huang He and the Chang Jiang.

   ___ The Himalayas in southwestern China are the highest mountains in the world.

2. **Read "Prehistoric Cultures" on pages 264 and 265. Which of the following is the best summary for this section? Check your answer.**

   ___ Like other great ancient civilizations, the earliest known Chinese civilization started along a river.

   ___ Two Neolithic farming cultures developed in China: the Yangshao along the Huang He river around 10,000 B.C., and the Lungshan in northeast China around 3000 B.C.

   ___ According to legend, the "Great Engineer" Yu founded the first great Chinese dynasty called the Xia around 2000 B.C.

3. **Read "Feudalism" on p. 268. Write a summary sentence for the section.**

   _____

   _____

   _____

   _____

Lesson 1 Summary
China's Early History

(*A Message of Ancient Days* pp. 262–269)

Thinking Focus: What advances were made by these ancient cultures—the Yangshao, the Lungshan, the Xia, the Shang, and the Zhou?

China's Geography

China's geography divides this vast country into many separate areas. For example, the southwestern part of China includes the Himalayas, the highest mountains in the world. The massive Gobi desert lies in the north. These and other landforms kept China isolated from the rest of the world for thousands of years. They also made travel and communication difficult within China. Although mountains and deserts divided China, rivers helped link many areas within the country. For example, farmers used rivers to send crops to ports on the Pacific Ocean.

[?] How did geography isolate ancient China from the rest of the world?

Prehistoric Cultures

By 10,000 B.C., a group of Neolithic people called the Yangshao had settled in north central China. They chose a place where one of China's major rivers, the Huang He, meets another river, the Wei. Archaeologists have discovered remains of Yangshao houses. They had plastered floors, and their roofs were held up by wooden posts.

A second Neolithic culture, the Lungshan, began in northeast China about 3000 B.C. The Lungshan harvested silk from silkworms, wove fabric, made pottery, and used simple written symbols. In order to farm near the river, they had to work together on flood control and irrigation projects.

[?] What were some achievements of China's Neolithic river cultures, the Yangshao and the Lungshan?

Summary continues on next page

Reading Support Resources

The Shang Dynasty

The Shang dynasty ruled China for over 700 years. During this time, most Shang people lived in farming villages, worked in the fields, and tried to control the flooding rivers. Rulers, priests, and warriors lived in cities surrounded by huge earth walls. Skilled craftsmen lived in neighborhoods outside the walls. In 1600 B.C., Shang craftsmen discovered how to make bronze, a strong metal. The Shang believed that the spirits of their **ancestors** controlled their lives. Shang kings used **oracle** bones to ask their ancestors questions about the future. The questions carved on these animal bones are the earliest known examples of Chinese writing.

? How did the Shang people live, and how did their religious beliefs affect their lives?

The Zhou Dynasty

The Zhou were farmers who lived in the Wei valley. In 1122 B.C., the Zhou overthrew the Shang. This began the Zhou dynasty, the longest dynasty in China's history. Zhou kings ruled China under a system called **feudalism.** Under the feudal system, nobles owned the land. A noble's land consisted of a walled town and the farms around it. Peasants paid the nobles so they could farm the land. In turn, the nobles paid the king and sent soldiers to help him in times of war.

During the Zhou period, teachers taught the people to read and write using pictures, or characters, to stand for words. So even though people across China spoke different **dialects**, they could communicate with each other through writing.

? In what ways were the Zhou walled cities like small countries?

ancestor
(ăn′sĕs′tər)

a relative who lived in the past

oracle
(ôr′ə-kəl)

a prediction about the future that comes from a god or ancestor

feudalism
(fyōōd′l-ĭz′əm)

an economic system in which nobles own the land and peasants work it

dialect
(dī′ə-lĕkt′)

a different form of the same language

CHAPTER 9

Lesson 2 Preview
The Age of Confucius

(A Message of Ancient Days pp. 270–274)

Chinese Belief Systems

	Confucianism	Moism	Legalism	Daoism
Human nature	good	good	bad	neither good nor bad
Government	rule by example like a good father	rule by men of learning	rule by strict laws	small and simple
Right conduct	sincerity, loyalty, kindness, respect	universal love	obedience to strict laws	in harmony with nature

1. **The graphic overview organizes information about four Chinese belief systems.**

   a. List the four belief systems.

   _____

   b. What three ideas of these belief systems can you compare and contrast, using this overview?

   _____

2. **Look at the chart on page 274, and read its caption. Then complete the sentences below.**

   a. The chart compares two schools of Chinese thought called

   _____ and _____ .

   b. The goal of Confucianism is _____ .

   c. The goal of Legalism is _____ .

   d. According to _____ , government should rule by law.

   e. According to _____ , government should rule by good example.

   f. Confucianism emphasizes the past, while Legalism is concerned with the _____ .

CHAPTER 9

Lesson 2 Reading Strategy
The Age of Confucius

(*A Message of Ancient Days* pp. 270–274)

Think About Words This reading strategy helps you figure out the meaning of new words. When you come to an unfamiliar word, look for word parts you already know and use clues such as context and pictures.

Read the paragraphs under the subheads listed below. Then follow the directions to develop a definition of *Confucianism.*

1. **Five Basic Relationships (pages 271–272)**

   a. List the three values that Confucius said are the foundation of relationships.

   _____

   b. What is the most important unit in Chinese society according to Confucius?

   _____

2. **Rulers and Their Subjects (page 272)**

   List two qualities of a good ruler, according to Confucius.

   _____

3. **Ideas About Government (page 272)**

   Answer these two questions:

   a. According to Confucianism, on what should government be based?

   _____

   b. How should government officials get their jobs?

   _____

4. **Use your answers to write a definition of *Confucianism.***

   _____

   _____

   _____

Lesson 2 Summary
The Age of Confucius

(*A Message of Ancient Days* pp. 270–274)

Thinking Focus: How did the teachings of Confucius compare with those of the Moists, the Legalists, and the Daoists?

An Age of Change

Over time, Chinese nobles and their armies gained power. In 771 B.C., powerful nobles invaded the Zhou capital, drove out its leaders, and became China's rulers. This was a time of unrest and great confusion.

Many great thinkers wanted to restore order to Chinese society. They tried to persuade the Chinese people and their rulers to accept their teachings and their view of how China should be ruled. One of the greatest thinkers was Confucius. Even today, Chinese people follow his teachings.

? Why did the Zhou kings lose their power, and who controlled China after them?

Confucius the Teacher

Confucius lived from 551 B.C. to 479 B.C. His family belonged to the **nobility**, although they were poor. Confucius studied hard and became one of the world's most successful teachers. His ideas, a code of behavior, are known as **Confucianism**. Here are some of his basic teachings:

- Kindness and goodness are very important.
- The foundation for every relationship, especially in families, should be sincerity, loyalty, and respect.
- If rulers are wise and good, then the people will also be wise and good.
- Government officials must earn their positions through education.

One hundred years after Confucius died, a follower, Mencius, spread the ideas of Confucianism throughout the country.

? What were some basic teachings of Confucius?

nobility
(nō-bĭl′ĭ-tē)
a class of people having high birth or rank

Confucianism
(kən-fyōō′shən-ĭz′əm)
Confucius's ideas on family, tradition, and respect

*Summary continues
on next page*

Opponents of Confucianism

In the last days of the Zhou dynasty, scholars, or educated people, argued about how the people should behave and how rulers should govern. Not all scholars supported the ideas and teachings of Confucianism. For example, one group, the Moists (MOH ihsts), believed that equal love for all people would bring peace. They believed that men of learning should be the rulers, not just guide the rulers. Another group, the Legalists, believed that people were bad and needed to have strict laws and harsh punishment. They believed that rulers needed to forget the past and be powerful, rather than just good. A third group, the Daoists, believed that people should live a simple, thoughtful life in harmony with nature. They had little interest in politics or government.

[?] In what ways did each of these groups—Moists, Legalists, and Daoists—disagree with Confucius?

Two Schools of Chinese Thought

	Confucianism	Legalism
Goal	Virtuous conduct, peaceful society	All power in the hands of the ruler
Government	Rule by good example	Rule by law, including rewards and punishments
Emphasis	The past	The present

CHAPTER 9

Lesson 3 Preview
A Unified China

(*A Message of Ancient Days* pp. 276–280)

China During the Qin Dynasty

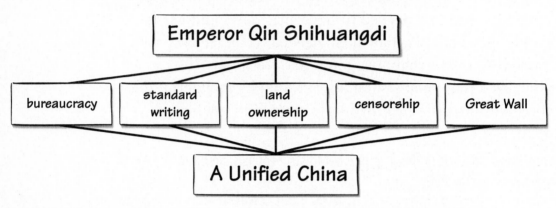

1. **Use the graphic overview to help you answer the following questions:**

   a. Emperor Qin Shihuangdi is credited with making five major changes in China. List the emperor's changes.

   _____

   _____

   b. What was the result of Emperor Qin Shihuangdi's changes?

   _____

   _____

2. **Look at the map on page 277. Use the map key to help you answer these questions. Circle your answers.**

   a. Is the Qin Dynasty of 221 B.C. larger or smaller in area than present-day China?

   larger   smaller

   b. What formed the northern boundary of the Qin Dynasty?

   Himalayas   Chang Jiang River   the Great Wall

   c. Which of the following cities is not located on a river?

   Xianyang   Beijing   Luoyang

CHAPTER 9

Lesson 3 Reading Strategy
A Unified China

(*A Message of Ancient Days* pp. 276–280)

Evaluate This reading strategy helps you recognize the difference between facts and opinions. A fact is something that can be proven to be true. An opinion is a belief based on what a person thinks or feels.

1. **Read "The Qin Dynasty" on page 277. Mark each sentence below with an *F* if it states a fact or with an *O* if it is an opinion.**

   ___ Being called king isn't a good enough title.

   ___ Qin Shihuangdi called himself the "first emperor."

   ___ The emperor's system of rewards and punishments was a good one.

   ___ The emperor's system of rewards and punishments strengthened his control.

2. **Write three more facts from "The Qin Dynasty" on page 277.**

   _____

   _____

   _____

3. **"The Legacy of Qin" on page 280 ends with this statement: "In a sense, Qin Shihuangdi, a brilliant and sometimes cruel emperor, gained the immortality he wanted." This statement includes three opinions. Often, an opinion is supported with facts. List a fact from this lesson for each of the three opinions.**

OPINION	SUPPORTED BY FACTS
Qin Shihuangdi was a brilliant emperor.	
Qin Shihuangdi was a cruel emperor.	
Qin Shihuangdi gained immortality.	

Lesson 3 Summary
A Unified China

(A Message of Ancient Days pp. 276–280)

Thinking Focus: How did Qin Shihuangdi unify China, and what did he do to maintain his empire?

The Qin Dynasty

The feudal state of Qin defeated the last Zhou ruler in 256 B.C. Twenty-five years later, the king of Qin led his state to victory over all other rulers and named himself Qin Shihuangdi—"first emperor of Qin." Qin Shihuangdi set out to bring all the warring states together. He divided his empire into 36 areas, called **provinces**, and divided each province into districts. Qin Shihuangdi appointed a governor and a defender for each province. They reported directly to him. Qin Shihuangdi also set up a system of rewards and punishments. As a result, the emperor strengthened his control and had the power to make great changes in his empire.

province
(prŏv′ĭns)
a territory governed as a unit with an empire

[?] What did Qin Shihuangdi hope to accomplish by appointing governors to rule the provinces?

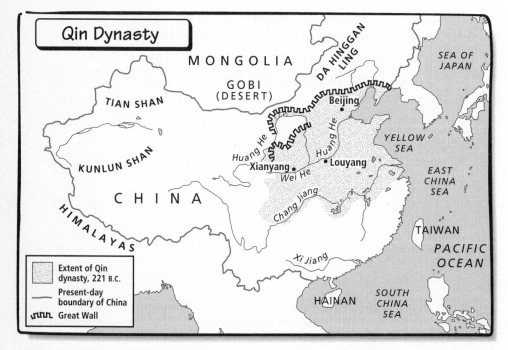

Qin Dynasty

MONGOLIA
GOBI (DESERT)
DA HINGGAN LING
SEA OF JAPAN
TIAN SHAN
Beijing
Huang He
Huang He
YELLOW SEA
KUNLUN SHAN
Xianyang
Louyang
Wei He
EAST CHINA SEA
CHINA
Chang Jiang
HIMALAYAS
TAIWAN
PACIFIC OCEAN
Xi Jiang
HAINAN
SOUTH CHINA SEA

Extent of Qin dynasty, 221 B.C.
Present-day boundary of China
Great Wall

Summary continues on next page

The Legacy of Qin

To strengthen his control and unify his empire, Qin Shihuangdi made many changes to the Chinese system. His new system would be used in China for centuries. It included the following changes:

- He set up a **bureaucracy** in which workers are appointed and trained for their jobs.
- He headed the bureaucracy and appointed three officials to hold the highest government and military positions.
- He made all measurement and money the same across the empire.
- He standardized the written characters so everyone could communicate.
- He took land away from the nobles, enabling any man to own land.
- He ordered the **censorship** of ideas and the burning of books that did not agree with him.
- He built the Great Wall of China to keep the peasants in and enemy invaders out.

[?] What are three things that Qin Shihuangdi standardized, and how did each change affect China?

bureaucracy
(byoo-rŏk′rə-sē)

an organization with one person at the top and many others at levels below

censorship
(sĕn′sər-shĭp′)

the control of what people read, write, see, or hear

CHAPTER 9
Lesson 4 Preview
The Han Dynasty

(A Message of Ancient Days pp. 281–287)

The Rule of the Han

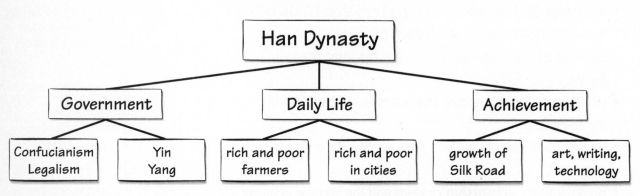

1. **Use the graphic overview to help you answer the questions below.**

   a. What three belief systems influenced the government of the Han Dynasty?

   _____

   b. In what two places did the Han people live their daily lives?

   _____

   c. The Han Dynasty made achievements in which four areas?

   _____

   _____

2. **Use the timeline on page 287 to find out when the following dynasties ruled China. Number the dynasties *1–5* in the order in which they occurred, starting with the oldest dynasty.**

   ___ Han Dynasty

   ___ Zhou Dynasty

   ___ Shang Dynasty

   ___ Legendary Xia Dynasty

   ___ Qin Dynasty

CHAPTER 9
Lesson 4 Reading Strategy
The Han Dynasty

(*A Message of Ancient Days* pp. 281–287)

Predict/Infer This reading strategy helps you understand what you have read and what you will read next. Before you read a section, think about the titles, pictures, and captions. Then think about what will happen in the selection.

1. **Look at the map on page 282. Compare this map with the one on page 277. What do you predict that you will learn about the Han dynasty?**

    ___ The empire of the Han dynasty was not as large as the empire of the Qin dynasty.

    ___ One achievement of the Han dynasty was expansion of the empire.

    ___ The Han dynasty stayed within the limits of the Great Wall.

2. **Find the main head on page 282. Write it here.**

    _____

    What prediction can you make about the government of the Han Dynasty?

    _____

3. **Look at the illustrations and read the captions on pages 284–287. Also read the main head and the subheads. What do you predict will be the achievements of the Han dynasty? Write your predictions in the chart below. Then read pages 284–287, and complete the chart.**

What I Predict	What I Found Out

CHAPTER 9
Lesson 4 Summary
The Han Dynasty

(A Message of Ancient Days pp. 281–287)

Thinking Focus: What kind of government did Han rulers create, and how did it affect people's lives?

Revival of Confucianism

As a Legalist, Qin Shihuangdi ruled harshly, and a few years after his death, the soldiers and peasants overthrew the Qin dynasty. This marked the beginning of the creative and scientific Han dynasty, whose rulers were in power from 206 B.C. to A.D. 220. Confucianism became popular again as the Han dynasty combined a strong ruler and strict law ideas of Legalism with the Confucian ideas of ruling with good example and not with punishment. Although the ideas of Legalism and Confucianism may seem opposite, the rulers of the Han dynasty understood Yin and Yang, the idea that opposites depend on each other, and that like day and night, opposites take turns.

? How did the Han and Qin governments differ?

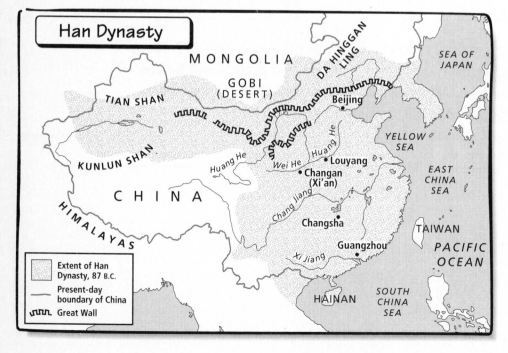

Han Dynasty

MONGOLIA
DA HINGGAN LING
SEA OF JAPAN
GOBI (DESERT)
Beijing
TIAN SHAN
YELLOW SEA
KUNLUN SHAN
Huang He
Wei He
Huang He
Louyang
Changan (Xi'an)
EAST CHINA SEA
CHINA
Chang Jiang
Changsha
TAIWAN
HIMALAYAS
PACIFIC OCEAN
Xi Jiang
Guangzhou
HAINAN
SOUTH CHINA SEA

Extent of Han Dynasty, 87 B.C.
Present-day boundary of China
Great Wall

Summary continues on next page

Daily Life in the Empire

Much like today, most of the Han Chinese people were farmers. Han farmers worked the fields together and lived in mud houses arranged in villages. Wealthy farmers had strong oxen to pull their carts and iron-tipped plows, and they watered their fields using simple machines. Poor farmers had no oxen, used wooden hand tools, and watered their fields by carrying buckets of water. Farmers in the north ate wheat and millet, while farmers in the south ate rice. They cooked their meals in a boxlike stove or steamed it over boiling water.

Rich and poor lived in the cities, which were centers of government, education, trade, and entertainment. The poor lived in houses that were close together. The rich lived in huge houses that were decorated with rugs and draperies.

? How were the lives of China's wealthy farmers different from the lives of poor farmers?

Achievements of the Han Dynasty

The Han dynasty marked the beginning of expansion and creativity. Emperor Wudi's armies expanded the empire by capturing lands to the south and crossing the Great Wall to the north. In 139 B.C., Wudi sent out the explorer Zhang Qian. He returned 10 years later with tales of Western riches and wonder. It was China's first hint that a civilized world lay beyond its borders, and it was the beginning of the trade route known as the Silk Road.

Han rulers kept their lands closed to outsiders. To do this, they used **middlemen** from neighboring countries to do their trading with other countries. They kept their achievements secret, such as the inventions of the **seismograph**, paper, and the medical practice of acupuncture. During the Han dynasty, Chinese engineers developed salt mining, and Chinese artisans worked with bronze and gold and they glazed pottery. Han dynasty writers wrote books on mathematics, medicine, poetry, history, and assembled the first Chinese dictionary.

? What were some of China's greatest achievements under the Han dynasty?

middleman
(mĭd′l-măn′)

a trader who buys from one and sells to another

seismograph
(sīz′mə-grăf′)

an instrument for detecting and determining the direction, strength, and lengths of earthquakes and other ground movements

Chapter Overview
The Ancient Israelites

Fill in the blank spaces below with information from the chapter.

When:
1900 B.C.– A.D. 135
Where:
Ancient Israel
Who:
Israelites

People of Biblical Times

Abraham → God commands him to start new nation

_____ → God gives him the name Israel

_____ → leads Israelites out of Egypt

David → defeats Goliath; unites tribes of Israel

_____ → builds the Temple in Jerusalem

Ezra → returns from exile in Babylon with Torah

the Maccabees → revolt and fight against Syrians

_____ → teachings become basis for Christianity

CHAPTER 10

Lesson 1 Preview
The Ancient Israelites

(A Message of Ancient Days pp. 298–303)

Events in Early Biblical History

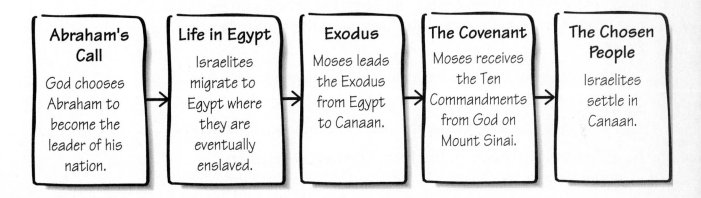

1. **Study the graphic overview. Then read the pairs of sentences below. Underline the sentence in each pair that tells what happened first.**

   a. Moses led the Exodus from Egypt to Canaan.

   God chose Abraham to lead his people.

   b. Moses received the Ten Commandments from God.

   The Egyptians enslaved the Israelites.

   c. The Israelites settled in Canaan.

   The Israelites migrated to Egypt.

2. **Look at the photograph on page 301 of your text. It shows the land through which the Israelites traveled during the Exodus from Egypt. Describe the land. Then tell what difficulties the Israelites probably faced.**

   _____

   _____

   _____

   _____

CHAPTER 10

Lesson 1 Reading Strategy
Early Biblical History

(*A Message of Ancient Days* pp. 298–303)

Finding the Main Idea This reading strategy helps you organize and remember what you read. When you finish a selection, jot down the main idea and its supporting details.

1. **Read "The Belief of the Israelites" on page 299. Which sentence below best expresses the main idea of the section? Write *M* next to your choice.**

    ___ The Torah contains the basic laws of Judaism and traces the history of Israel.

    ___ Many people today follow the beliefs of the ancient Israelites.

    ___ Judaism, the religion of the Jewish people, is based on monotheism, the belief that there is only one true God.

2. **Read from the beginning of "The Origin of the Israelites" on page 299 through the first paragraph on page 301. Which sentence below best expresses the main idea of the section? Write *M* next to your choice.**

    ___ Canaan was an important trading route, market, and battlefield.

    ___ Today this area is no longer called Canaan.

    ___ The new nation of Israel was begun in Canaan by the descendants of Abraham.

3. **Read "The Leadership of Moses" on page 301. Then fill in the chart below.**

Main Idea	Supporting Details

Lesson 1 Summary
Early Biblical History

(A Message of Ancient Days pp. 298–303)

Thinking Focus: What role did the Israelites' relationship with God play in the formation of their nation?

The Belief of the Israelites

The Israelites believed that they were the chosen people, and that God had delivered them from Egypt. Unlike other ancient peoples, the Israelites believed in *only* one God. This belief in one God is called **monotheism.** The story of the development of the Israelites is found in the Torah. The Torah contains the religious teachings of **Judaism.** It also traces the history of the Israelites through the 1200s B.C.

? What is monotheism?

The Origins of the Israelites

According to the Torah, God told Abraham, a Mesopotamian shepherd, to migrate to Canaan. Abraham's descendants, known as Hebrews, were nomadic herders. Abraham had a grandson named Jacob. Jacob's name was changed to Israel, which means "one who wrestles with God." His descendants were known as Israelites.

The Torah says that famines in Canaan caused some Israelites to migrate to Egypt, where they became slaves. They suffered in slavery for more than 400 years before finding a strong leader in Moses. According to the Torah, God gave Moses miraculous powers to help him free the Israelites. Many horrible plagues, or outbreaks of disease and destruction, fell upon the Egyptians. When a 10th plague killed the oldest male child of every Egyptian family, the pharaoh finally freed the Israelites. Moses led them in the long journey back to Canaan. This journey is known as the **Exodus.**

monotheism
(mŏn′ə-thē-ĭz′əm)
the belief that there is only one God

Judaism
(jōō′dē-ĭz′əm)
the monotheistic religion of the Jewish people

Exodus
(ĕk′sə-dəs)
the departure of the Israelites from Egypt

*Summary continues
on next page*

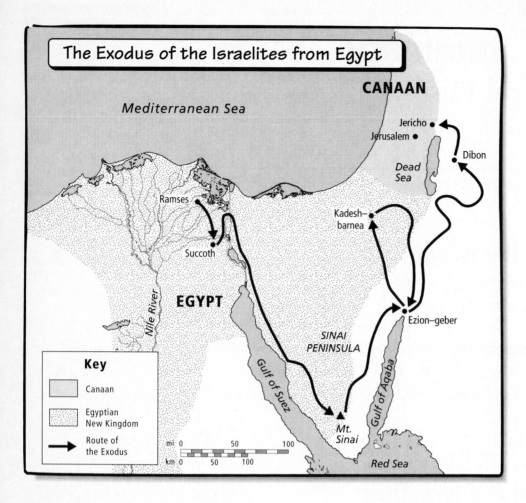

The Exodus of the Israelites from Egypt

[?] Trace the origins of the Israelites.

An Agreement with God

The Torah teaches that during the Exodus, Moses received a message from God about a **covenant**, or agreement. According to this covenant, God would love and protect the Israelites. They, in turn, must love God and obey God's laws. The most important of these laws were the Ten Commandments. These commandments form the basis of much of the Western world's ideas about law and justice.

[?] Why did the Israelites agree to obey the Ten Commandments?

covenant
(kŭv′ə-nənt)

an agreement between people; an agreement between people and their God

CHAPTER 10

Lesson 2 Preview
Kings, Prophets, and Priests

(*A Message of Ancient Days* pp. 308–314)

Political History of the Israelites

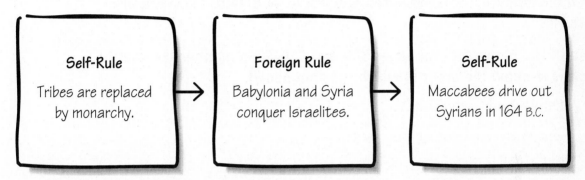

Self-Rule	Foreign Rule	Self-Rule
Tribes are replaced by monarchy.	Babylonia and Syria conquer Israelites.	Maccabees drive out Syrians in 164 B.C.

1. **Look at the graphic overview. Then read each statement below. Write *T* if the statement is true. Write *F* if it is false.**

   a. ____ The Israelites have always enjoyed self-rule.

   b. ____ The Israelites conquered Babylonia and Syria.

   c. ____ Babylonia and Syria conquered the Israelites.

   d. ____ The Maccabees drove out the Babylonians in 164 B.C.

   e. ____ The Maccabees drove out the Syrians in 164 B.C.

2. **Look at the pictures and captions on page 314. What does the lighting of the menorah represent?**

   _____

   _____

   _____

CHAPTER 10

Lesson 2 Reading Strategy
Kings, Prophets, and Priests

(*A Message of Ancient Days* pp. 308–314)

Sequence This reading strategy helps you follow what is happening in your reading. As you read, pay attention to dates and times, as well as to words such as *before, finally, after,* and *then.*

1. **Read "The Monarchy" on pages 309 and 310. Then number the events below to show the order in which they happened.**

   ___ David built a dynasty.

   ___ The Assyrians conquered Israel.

   ___ Solomon built a magnificent temple.

   ___ The Babylonians conquered Judah.

2. **Read "A People Governed by Priests" on pages 311 and 312. Put the following events in order.**

   ___ Cyrus allowed the Jews to return to Judah.

   ___ Ezra brought the Torah from Babylon.

   ___ Cyrus the Great took control of Babylon.

3. **Read pages 313 and 314. Complete the timeline below by filling in the blanks.**

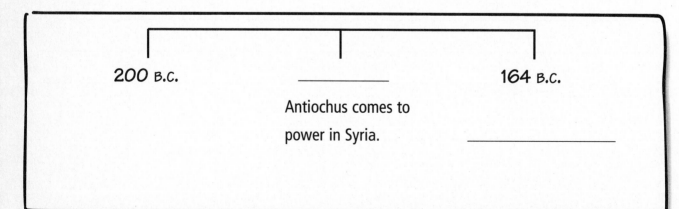

200 B.C.   _____   164 B.C.

Antiochus comes to
power in Syria.   _____

Lesson 2 Summary
Kings, Prophets, and Priests

(*A Message of Ancient Days* pp. 308–314)

Thinking Focus: How did Israel develop as an independent Jewish nation?

The Monarchy

Fighting with other groups in Canaan led the Israelites to realize that they needed a king to lead them. The first three kings were:

- Saul, who led the fight against a Canaanite group called the Philistines but was unable to defeat them;
- David, who defeated the Philistines and made Jerusalem the capital of Israel;
- Solomon, who made treaties with the pharaoh of Egypt and other rulers, increased trade, and began a royal building program.

When Solomon died in 922 B.C., Israel was a strong nation. But the people were heavily taxed. The tribes in the north revolted and chose their own king. They moved their capital to Samaria. The northern kingdom continued to be called Israel. The southern kingdom was called Judah.

For 200 years, the two kingdoms existed side by side. Then, in 721 B.C., the Assyrians conquered Israel. In 587 B.C., the Babylonians conquered Judah.

[?] What caused Israel to be divided into two kingdoms?

The Message of the Prophets

When the Babylonians conquered Judah, they destroyed Jerusalem. They took 15,000 Jews to Babylonia as prisoners. The **prophets** told the Jews that they had only themselves to blame, for they had broken their covenant with God. But the prophets also preached that if the Jews obeyed God's laws, they would someday be able to return to their homeland.

[?] According to the prophets, why was Judah captured by Babylonia?

prophet
(prŏf′ ĭt)

a person who expresses the will of God

Summary continues on next page

A People Governed by Priests

The Babylonian exile lasted for about 50 years. Then Cyrus the Great of Persia conquered Babylonia and allowed the Jews to return to Judah. Led by their priests, the Jews rebuilt the great temple in Jerusalem. But Judah remained a Persian province.

In the 400s B.C., a priest named Ezra returned from Babylonia with a collection of holy writings. This document was the Torah, the sacred history and laws of the Israelites. Now the Jews had a temple and the Torah. But they did not have independence. They hoped for a **messiah** who would come and free them.

[?] How was the Torah of central importance to the Jews?

messiah
(mə-sī'ə)
the hoped-for king who would free the Jewish people and bring world peace

The Revolt of the Maccabees

Around 200 B.C., the Syrians took over the Jews, bringing ideas from Greek culture. The ruler Antiochus tried to force the Jews to worship Greek gods. A Jewish priest named Mattathias organized a revolt. Led by his son Judah Maccabee, the rebels fought a two-year war to overcome the Syrians. In 164 B.C., the "Maccabees" drove the Syrians out of the region around Jerusalem. The Jews had control of their temple again. The Jewish festival of Chanukah celebrates the victory of the Maccabees.

[?] What was the result of the revolt of the Maccabees?

CHAPTER 10

Lesson 3 Preview
Religious Developments

(A Message of Ancient Days pp. 315–321)

The Contributions of Judaism and Christianity

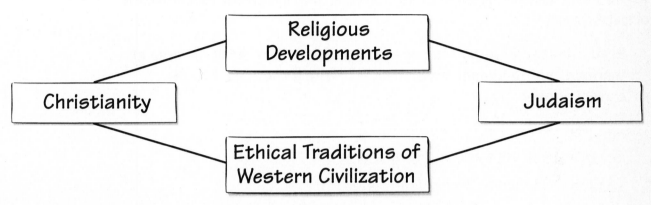

1. **Look at the graphic overview. Then write** *Christianity* **or** *Judaism* **to answer each question below.**

   a. Under which heading would you put information about the life of Jesus? _____

   b. Under which heading would you put information about the revolt against Rome and the fall of Masada? _____

2. **Look at the chart on page 319. Name the religion and the holy day associated with each of the events listed below.**

   a. the rededication of the Temple _____

   b. the birth of Jesus _____

   c. the Resurrection of Jesus _____

   d. the Exodus of the Israelites from Egypt _____

   e. the descent of the Holy Spirit on the Apostles _____

   f. the creation of the world _____

CHAPTER 10
Lesson 3 Reading Strategy
Religious Developments

(*A Message of Ancient Days* pp. 315–321)

Cause and Effect This reading strategy helps you understand events and why they occur. As you read, think about the factors that caused an event. Then think about what the effects of that event may be.

1. Read "The Life of Jesus" on pages 316 and 317. Why did Jesus base his teachings on traditional Jewish beliefs? Write a check next to the correct answer.

    ___ Jesus converted to Judaism as a young man.

    ___ Jesus was born and raised as a Jew.

    ___ Jesus claimed to be the son of God.

2. Read "The Teachings of Jesus" on pages 317 and 318. Jesus gained many followers among the Jews. Why did this upset the Romans?

    ___ Jesus disagreed with some aspects of Roman law.

    ___ The Romans did not want him to heal the sick.

    ___ The Romans thought he might cause a revolt.

3. Read "The Jewish Legacy" on pages 320 and 321. Then complete the chart below by telling how each of the things listed in the left-hand column helped Jews adapt to their new situation.

Causes	Effects
the Torah	
rabbis	
synagogues	

Lesson 3 Summary
Religious Developments

(*A Message of Ancient Days* pp. 315–321)

Thinking Focus: How are Judaism and Christianity related?

The Teachings of Jesus

A Jewish teacher named Jesus attracted followers in the first
century A.D. He preached that the kingdom of God had come.
The kingdom of God is God's power and victory over evil. Jesus
taught some traditional Jewish beliefs, such as the rules to love
God and your neighbor. He often used **parables** to explain
his ideas.

The Romans feared that Jesus might cause a revolt. In about
A.D. 33, his opponents brought Jesus before the Roman governor,
Pontius Pilate. They charged him with treason. Pilate ordered
that Jesus be put to death by crucifixion. According to the New
Testament, three days after his death, Jesus arose from the dead.
This event is called the **Resurrection**, and it forms an important
tenet of **Christianity**.

? What did Jesus teach about the kingdom of God?

Judaism in the First Century

At the time of Jesus' death, Rome ruled Judea, as Judah was
now called. In A.D. 66, a group of Jews known as Zealots
rebelled against Roman rule. Like the Maccabees, they used hit-
and-run tactics against the Romans. Finally, to bring the rebels
under control, a Roman general named Titus attacked Jerusalem.
The Jews held out for five months, but finally the city fell. The
Romans burned the temple and destroyed the city.

Other centers of Jewish resistance held out for three more
years. The Great Revolt ended with the fall of Masada. Many
Jews were enslaved and taken to other parts of the Roman
Empire. The scattering of Jewish settlements is called the

parable
(păr′ə-bəl)

a story that teaches a
moral or religious lesson

Resurrection
(rĕz′ə-rĕk′shən)

the rising of Jesus on the
third day after his death

Christianity
(krĭs′chē-ăn′ĭ-tē)

the Christian religion,
founded on the
teachings of Jesus

*Summary continues
on next page*

Diaspora. The Jews attempted another revolt in A.D. 132 but were again defeated. This time, they were prohibited from living in Jerusalem.

[?] How did the Jews revolt against the Romans?

The Jewish Legacy

The Jews had lost their temple, their priests, and their homeland. But as a people, they and their religion survived. Here are three reasons why:

- The Jews held onto their religion by relying on the Torah.
- They continued to learn from their **rabbis** and to practice Jewish traditions.
- They built **synagogues** in which to worship and to study the Torah.

The Jews developed ways of practicing their religion and ideas of social justice that are still used today.

[?] How did the Jewish religion survive after the Roman attacks?

Diaspora
(dī-ăs′pər-ə)
the Jewish settlements scattered among the Gentiles

rabbi
(răb′ī)
the leader of a Jewish congregation

synagogue
(sĭn′ə-gŏg′)
a meeting place for Jewish worship and instruction

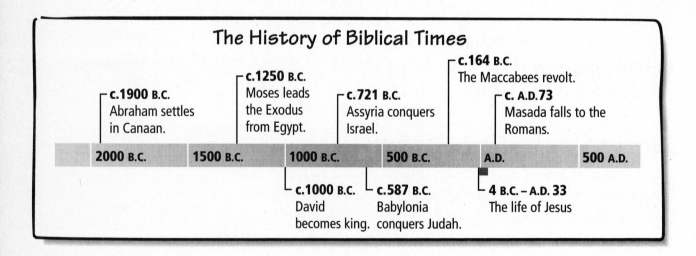

The History of Biblical Times

c.1900 B.C.
Abraham settles in Canaan.

c.1250 B.C.
Moses leads the Exodus from Egypt.

c.721 B.C.
Assyria conquers Israel.

c.164 B.C.
The Maccabees revolt.

C. A.D.73
Masada falls to the Romans.

| 2000 B.C. | 1500 B.C. | 1000 B.C. | 500 B.C. | A.D. | 500 A.D. |

c.1000 B.C.
David becomes king.

c.587 B.C.
Babylonia conquers Judah.

4 B.C. – A.D. 33
The life of Jesus

Chapter Overview
The Ancient Greeks

Fill in the blank spaces below with information from the chapter.

History of Ancient Greece

When:
2500 B.C.–479 B.C.

Where:
Ancient Greece

Who:
Early Greeks

Cause

| Mountains and _____ |

→

Effect

| Rise of independent city-states and sea travel |

| Citizens share power |

→

| Development of _____ |

| Worship of _____ |

→

| Myths, sanctuaries, and festivals |

| Uniting of Sparta and Athens |

→

| Defeat of _____ |

CHAPTER 11

Lesson 1 Preview
The Early Greeks

(*A Message of Ancient Days* pp. 328–333)

Early Greece

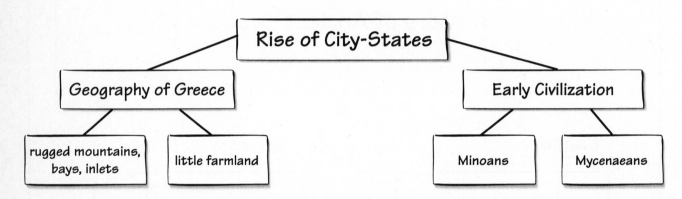

1. **Look at the graphic overview. Use the overview to answer the questions below.**

   a. Describe the geography of Greece.

   _____

   _____

   b. What are the names of two civilizations that came before Greek city-states?

   _____

   _____

2. **Look at the map on page 333 of your text. Which statement best describes the location of the Greek city-states? Circle the letter next to your answer.**

   a. Most city-states were located far from the sea.

   b. Mountains, water, and jagged coastlines separated Greek city-states from each other.

   c. Greece is a flat land, and city-states were located on lots of farmland.

   d. There were no city-states on the islands of Greece.

CHAPTER 11

Lesson 1 Reading Strategy
The Early Greeks

(*A Message of Ancient Days* pp. 328–333)

Sequence This reading strategy helps you follow what is happening in your reading. As you read, pay attention to dates and times, as well as to words such as *before, finally, after,* and *then.*

1. **Read the paragraph under the main head "Early Civilizations" on page 331. Also read the paragraphs under "Minoan Civilization."**

   a. What are the beginning and ending dates of the Minoan Age?

   _____

   b. List three accomplishments of the Minoans.

   _____

   _____

   _____

2. **Now read "Mycenaean Civilization" on page 332.**

   a. When did the Mycenaeans conquer the Minoans?_____

   b. What are the beginning and end dates of the Mycenaean Age?_____

3. **Read "The Dark Age" on page 332. What are the beginning and end dates of the period called the Dark Age?**_____

4. **Number the following events to show the order in which they happened.**

   ___ Homer wrote the *Odyssey.*

   ___ Greeks began to write again.

   ___ Mycenae fell to invaders.

Lesson 1 Summary
The Early Greeks

(*A Message of Ancient Days* pp. 328–333)

Thinking Focus: What were some of the forces that influenced the rise of civilization in ancient Greece?

The Land Around the Sea

The ancient Greeks settled on the mountainous peninsula called the Peloponnesus. They also settled on islands in the Aegean Sea. Mountains and water divided Greece into many regions. But the sea also connected these regions with each other and with other cultures. The ancient Greeks were sailors and traders. They sailed west to Sicily and east to the Black Sea to trade goods such as grapes, grain, and olives. They also made contact with other peoples, such as the Egyptians, Phoenicians, and Persians. New ideas from these cultures helped Greek civilization to develop.

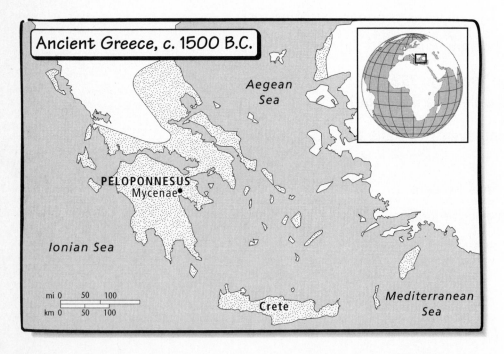

Ancient Greece, c. 1500 B.C.

Aegean Sea

PELOPONNESUS
Mycenae

Ionian Sea

Crete

Mediterranean Sea

mi 0   50   100
km 0   50   100

[?] How did sea trade influence the growth of civilization in Greece?

*Summary continues
on next page*

The Early Greeks *(Lesson 1 Summary continued)*

Early Civilizations

The roots of Greek civilization can be traced to two nearby cultures. These cultures were the Minoans and the Mycenaeans.

The Minoans lived on the island of Crete. They were great artists, sailors, and city builders. The Mycenaeans lived in the mountains on the Greek mainland. They learned how to build cities from the Minoans. They also adopted the Minoan system of writing. Like the Minoans, they were great sailors and builders.

In about 1450 B.C., the Mycenaeans conquered the Minoans. The Mycenaeans ruled the Aegean region for about 300 years. In the 1100s B.C., Mycenaean culture began to decline. This decline was called the Dark Age. Written language disappeared, and people became isolated from each other. Then, in 800 B.C., the Greeks began to write again. Once again, storytellers retold the legends and myths of their past.

? What did the Minoan and Mycenaean civilizations have in common?

The Rise of the City-States

Greece's Dark Age ended around 800–750 B.C. Cities grew. Trade increased. People in neighboring cities got together and traded with one another. Leaders arose among the people in each city, until each city became like a separate small country or state. These cities were called **city-states**. Some city-states became so big that they needed more farmland to support their people. This led to fights between neighboring city-states over territory. Greek colonists also left their city-states to found new ones. Greek city-states flourished in the 600s and 500s B.C., a period known as the Age of Expansion.

? What was the Age of Expansion?

city-state
(sit 'E-stAt')
a self-governing unit made up of a city and its surrounding area

© Houghton Mifflin Company. All rights reserved.

Reading Support Resources

Lesson Summary • **Chapter 11, Lesson 1**   **159**

CHAPTER 11

Lesson 2 Preview

Athens: A City-State

(*A Message of Ancient Days* pp. 338–343)

The Road to Democracy

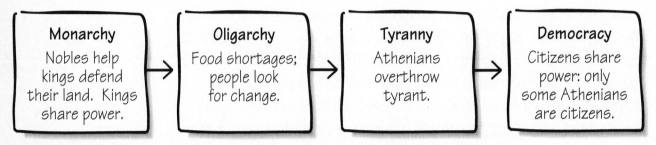

| Monarchy | Oligarchy | Tyranny | Democracy |
| Nobles help kings defend their land. Kings share power. | Food shortages; people look for change. | Athenians overthrow tyrant. | Citizens share power; only some Athenians are citizens. |

1. **The graphic overview shows different types of government in Athens. List the four types of government in the order in which they developed.**

    a. _____

    b. _____

    c. _____

    d. _____

2. **Find the words listed below in "The Evolution of Democracy" on pages 339 and 340. Use the sentence in which each word appears to help you write a definition for each word.**

    a. democracy:

    _____

    b. monarchy:

    _____

    c. oligarchy:

    _____

    d. tyrant:

    _____

CHAPTER 11

Lesson 2 Reading Strategy
Athens: A City-State

(*A Message of Ancient Days* pp. 338–343)

Compare and Contrast This reading strategy helps you understand how events are similar and different. As you read about historical events, think about how they compare and contrast with events you already know.

1. **Read "The Origins of Democracy" on pages 339 and 340. Write *D* before each statement below that is a disadvantage for the people under the rule of an oligarchy. Write *A* if it is an advantage.**

   a. ___ Poor farmers lost land to the wealthy people.

   b. ___ The king shared power with the nobles.

   c. ___ There were food shortages.

   d. ___ The government of the Greek city-states improved.

2. **Read "The Rule of Tyrants" on pages 340 and 341. Write *D* before each statement below that is a disadvantage for the people under the rule of tyranny. Write *A* if it is an advantage.**

   a. ___ The tyrant promoted building projects and festivals.

   b. ___ Some tyrants were harsh and greedy.

   c. ___ People learned that they could make changes.

3. **Read "The Democracy of Athens" on pages 341 and 342. Then read "Citizenship in Athens" and "The Economy of Athens" on pages 342 and 343. Below, write two advantages and two disadvantages of Greek democracy.**

Advantages of Greek Democracy	Disadvantages of Greek Democracy
1.	1.
2.	2.

Lesson 2 Summary
Athens: A City-State

(*A Message of Ancient Days* pp. 338–343)

Summary also on
Audiotape

Thinking Focus: How did democracy develop and work in Athens?

The Evolution of Democracy

Between the 700s and 400s B.C., the people of Athens developed a new kind of government. This form of government, called **democracy**, gave the people the power to rule and make decisions.

Before democracy, Greece was governed by three different systems: **monarchy**, **oligarchy**, and the rule of **tyrants**.

- In a monarchy, a king rules over the people. During the Dark Age, most city-states were ruled by a king.
- In an oligarchy, a small group of people rules over everyone else. At the end of the Dark Age, a small group of nobles shared power equally with the king in many city-states.
- A tyrant is a leader who seizes power by force. During the 500s B.C., tyrants came to power because people were not happy with oligarchies.

[?] Trace the development of democracy from the monarchy.

Citizenship in Athens

In Athens, all citizens could take part in the government. But not everyone could be a citizen. Rules for citizenship were strict. You had to be male and over 18. Usually your father, and sometimes your mother's father, had to be a citizen. Women and children could not be citizens. Foreigners living in Athens, called metics, could not become citizens, although they were protected by Athenian law. Slaves could not be citizens. They also couldn't vote, choose their jobs, or have a family without their master's permission.

democracy
(dĭ-mŏk′rə-sē)

a system of government in which the people rule

monarchy
(mŏn′ər-kē)

a system of government in which a monarch, such as a king, is the ruler

oligarchy
(ŏl′ĭ-gär′kē)

a system of government in which a few people rule

tyrant
(tī′rənt)

a ruler who has total power, not limited by a constitution or other officials

*Summary continues
on next page*

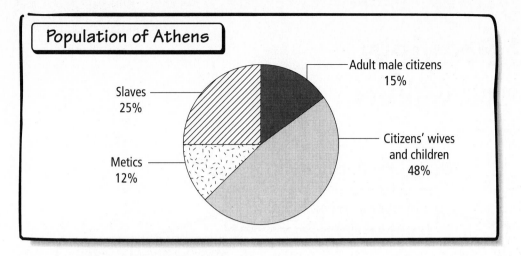

? Find evidence in the lesson to disprove this statement: In Athens everyone took part in the government.

The Economy of Athens

Until the 500s B.C., Athenians did most of their trading through **barter**. For example, they might trade grain for olives. Around 570 B.C., the government started making gold and silver coins. Coins were better than bartering because you could exchange them for any product. The use of coins made Athens wealthy.

Wealthy Athenians had to give large sums of money to the government to fund projects like building ships and staging religious festivals. These projects gave work to merchants and craftsmen. In this way, more Athenians shared in the city's wealth.

? Why did wealthy families in Athens have difficulty staying rich?

barter
(bär′tər)

a system of trade in which goods are exchanged instead of money

CHAPTER 11
Lesson 3 Preview
Ancient Greek Culture
(*A Message of Ancient Days* pp. 345–350)

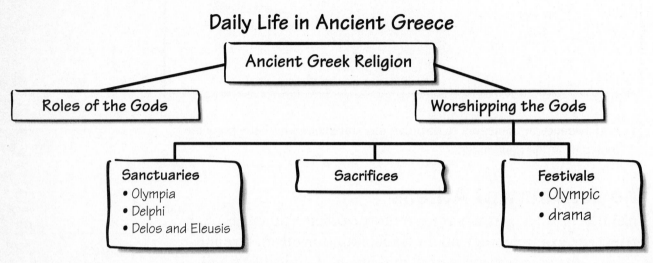

Daily Life in Ancient Greece

1. **The graphic overview shows that Lesson 3 has information about two major aspects of ancient Greek religion.**

   a. What are the two aspects?

   _____

   b. The gods were worshiped through festivals. What two kinds of festivals does the overview name?

   _____

2. **Look at the map on page 348.**

   a. Use the map key to find four major Greek sanctuaries. List their names here.

   _____

   b. Which sanctuary is located on an island in the Aegean Sea?

   _____

   c. Which sanctuary is located near Athens?

   _____

   d. Look at the inset map. What is the name of the temple at the center of this sanctuary?

   _____

CHAPTER 11

Lesson 3 Reading Strategy
Ancient Greek Culture

(A Message of Ancient Days **pp. 345–350)**

Self-Question   This reading strategy helps you stay focused on what you read. Ask yourself questions before you read a section. Then read to see if you can find the answer to your questions.

1. **Find the main head at the top of page 346. Write it here.**

   _____

2. **Which question below would you expect this section to answer?**

   ___ Who were the members of the family of Greek gods?

   ___ Who was the strongest Greek god?

   ___ What was ancient Greek culture?

3. **Read page 346. Was the question you chose answered? If so, write the answer. If not, choose another question that is answered. Write the answer.**

   _____

   _____

   _____

4. **Find the main heads on pages 347 and 350. Use the chart to write a question you think will be answered in the paragraphs under each head. Now read those paragraphs. Write your answer to each question. If you do not find an answer, you may want to revise the question.**

page 347: Sanctuaries to the Gods	page 350: Greek Drama
Q.	Q.
A.	A.

Lesson 3 Summary
Ancient Greek Culture

(*A Message of Ancient Days* pp. 345–350)

Thinking Focus: What religious beliefs and customs did all Greeks share?

The Family of Greek Gods

The Greeks worshiped Zeus and his family of gods. The Greeks celebrated their gods in myths and legends that explained how these gods created the world and controlled nature. The gods of Greek myths formed a family, and each member had a special role and special powers. For example:

- Zeus, master of the world, was the god of justice and controlled the weather.
- Poseidon, Zeus's brother, was god of the sea.
- Hera, Zeus's wife, was goddess of marriage.
- Dionysus was the god of wine.
- Apollo, Dionysus's son, was the god of light. He drove the sun across the sky each day in his chariot.

The Greeks prayed to specific gods for things they wanted, and they thanked the gods by making animal sacrifices when their prayers were answered.

[?] Describe some of the Greek gods and their powers.

Sanctuaries to the Gods

The Greeks built sacred places called **sanctuaries** to honor their gods. There were four major sanctuaries in Greece: Olympia, Delphi, Delos, and Eleusis. Each sanctuary was built in an area of natural beauty. The Greeks used these sacred places to make animal sacrifices to the gods. They also used sanctuaries to learn hidden knowledge from the gods. The shrines where these messages from the gods were revealed were called oracles. The Greeks also used sanctuaries to hold religious festivals.

[?] How did the Greek people use sanctuaries?

sanctuary
(săngk'chōo-ĕr'ē)

a place of worship such as a church, temple, or mosque

Summary continues on next page

Reading Support Resources

Greek Drama

One special Greek festival honored the god of wine, Dionysus. This was a drama festival, where plays were performed from dawn until dark for four days. Two drama festivals were held in Athens each year. Some of the plays performed in ancient Athens are still performed today. **Tragedies** told stories of heroes who were brought to ruin by a flaw in their character. **Comedies** made fun of such things as politics and everyday life. Thousands of people would watch the plays. Judges would award ivy crowns to the writers of the winning plays.

? How was the festival of Dionysus different from the festivals to other gods?

tragedy
(trăj′ĭ-dē)

a serious drama in which the hero is defeated by a character flaw

comedy
(kŏm′ĭ-dē)

a humorous play that has a happy ending

CHAPTER 11
Lesson 4 Preview
A Tale of Two City-States

(A Message of Ancient Days pp. 351–357)

Comparing Athens and Sparta

	Government	Economy	Education
Sparta	oligarchy	military	emphasized military and discipline
Athens	democracy	farming and trade	emphasized culture, physical and liberal education

1. **The graphic overview compares the two city-states of Sparta and Athens. Use it to answer the questions below.**

   a. Which city-state had a democratic form of government?

   _____

   b. Which city-state had an economy based on farming and trade?

   _____

   c. Which city-state emphasized military training?

   _____

2. **Look at the pictograph on page 352. Use it to complete these sentences.**

   a. The Spartan government was an oligarchy ruled by

   _____ and _____ .

   b. The kings joined 28 others to make up the next level, called the

   _____ .

   c. All Spartan citizens belonged to the Citizen's

   _____ .

CHAPTER 11

Lesson 4 Reading Strategy
A Tale of Two City-States

(*A Message of Ancient Days* pp. 351–357)

Using the Visuals This reading strategy helps you use photographs, maps, charts, and illustrations to help you understand what you read. As you read, be sure to study the visuals and carefully read the captions.

1. **Look at the photographs of the sculptures on pages 352 and 353. Read the captions. Put a check beside the information you can learn from these sculptures. You may choose more than one sentence.**

   ___ The clothing of the Spartans was black.

   ___ Spartan people were exceptionally tall.

   ___ Spartans in the 500s B.C. were accomplished bronze sculptors.

   ___ Spartan craftsmen used their art to show warriors and athletes.

2. **Use the chart on page 354 to answer these questions.**

   a. What was the life of a 14-year-old Spartan boy like?

   _____

   _____

   b. What was the life of a 14-year-old Athenian girl like?

   _____

   _____

3. **Look at the diagrams of the Battle of Salamis on pages 356 and 357. Read the captions. Then write several sentences about what you learned.**

   _____

   _____

   _____

   _____

Lesson 4 Summary
A Tale of Two City-States

(*A Message of Ancient Days* pp. 351–357)

Thinking Focus: How were the cultures of Athens and Sparta similar? How were they different?

Sparta and Athens

Athens and Sparta were the two largest city-states in Greece. Sparta was invaded and conquered by the Dorians around 1100 B.C. All former Spartans were made slaves. Because there were many more slaves than citizens, Sparta built a strong army to protect themselves from a slave uprising. Most Spartan men spent their lives in the army.

Sparta began as a monarchy, but it had two kings who ruled together. In time, the two kings became part of a 30-man senate. All Spartan citizens belonged to an assembly similar to the one in Athens. The assembly elected five **ephors**, or leaders. But although the Spartans had an assembly and held elections, power was really in the hands of a few families. A truly democratic government never developed in Sparta. Sparta remained an oligarchy.

Spartans led simple lives. Each citizen received a plot of land from the government. Slaves called **helots** farmed the land.

? Why did the economy of Sparta center on a strong army?

ephor
(ĕf′ôr′)

one of five elected officials who supervised the kings of ancient Sparta

helot
(hĕl′ət)

a state slave in ancient Sparta

Education in Sparta and Athens

In Sparta, boys lived with boys their own age and were taught reading, writing, and athletics. At age 18, young men went into the army. Girls received less education than boys, but they did get physical training.

In Athens, the wealthy boys went to school, but they continued to live at home. They learned reading, writing, arithmetic, poetry, music, dance, and athletics. At age 18, young men joined the army

Summary continues on next page

for two years and then served only in times of war. Girls learned crafts and poetry from their mothers.

[?] How did education differ in Sparta and in Athens?

Allies Against Persia

Sparta and Athens joined together during the Persian Wars. The wars began when the Persian Empire began to take over city-states along the Aegean Sea. Athens sent soldiers to help the city-states and was defeated. But in 490 B.C., Athens defeated Persia near the town of Marathon. The Persian leader Xerxes and his army returned 10 years later. The Persians overran Greece and burned Athens. But in a battle off the coast of Salamis, the Greeks sank half the Persian ships. In 479 B.C. the Greeks defeated the Persians. By banding together, the Greek city-states were able to defeat the huge Persian army.

Battles of the Persian Wars

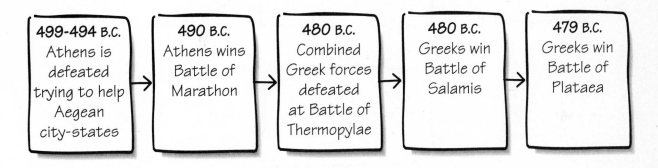

| 499-494 B.C. Athens is defeated trying to help Aegean city-states | 490 B.C. Athens wins Battle of Marathon | 480 B.C. Combined Greek forces defeated at Battle of Thermopylae | 480 B.C. Greeks win Battle of Salamis | 479 B.C. Greeks win Battle of Plataea |

[?] How did the Greeks finally win the Persian Wars?

Chapter Overview
Classical Greece

Fill in the blank spaces below with information from the chapter.

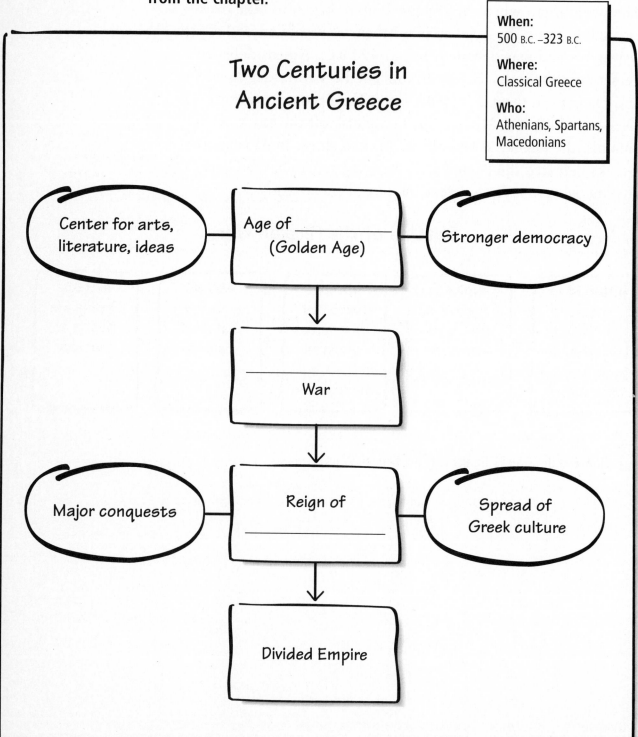

Two Centuries in
Ancient Greece

When:
500 B.C. –323 B.C.

Where:
Classical Greece

Who:
Athenians, Spartans,
Macedonians

Center for arts,
literature, ideas

Age of _____
(Golden Age)

Stronger democracy

_____
War

Major conquests

Reign of
_____

Spread of
Greek culture

Divided Empire

CHAPTER 12
Lesson 1 Preview
The Golden Age of Athens

(*A Message of Ancient Days* pp. 362–368)

Pericles' Goals for Athens

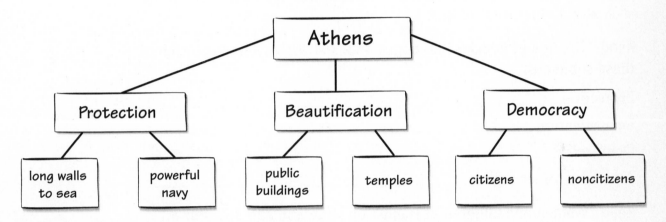

1. **Look at the graphic overview. Then use it to complete the sentences below.**

   a. To protect Athens, Pericles wanted to build a powerful navy.
   He also wanted to build _____.

   b. To beautify the city, Pericles wanted Athenians to construct
   public buildings. He also wanted Athenians to build _____.

   c. Pericles wanted to strengthen Athenian democracy. He wanted to
   make life better for both _____ and _____.

2. **The two pictures on page 366 of your text show Greek women performing three different jobs. What are those jobs?**

   _____

   _____

   _____

CHAPTER 12

Lesson 1 Reading Strategy
The Golden Age of Athens

(*A Message of Ancient Days* pp. 362–368)

Evaluate This reading strategy helps you recognize the difference between facts and opinions. A fact is something that can be proven to be true. An opinion is a belief that is based on what a person thinks or feels.

1. **Read "The Age of Pericles" on pages 362–364. Write a fact for each of these subheads:**

   Protection_____

   Beautification _____

   Democracy_____

   Athens's Golden Age _____

2. **Read "Women and Children at Home" on page 366 and 367. Put a check mark next to any statement below that is a fact.**

   ___ Women worked at spinning, dying, and weaving.

   ___ Athenian children were treated unfairly.

   ___ The juries in the law courts included too many people.

3. **Read "Men at the Marketplace" on pages 365 and 366. Fill in the chart below with at least three facts from the section. Add three of your own opinions about those facts.**

Facts	My Opinions
(1)	(1)
(2)	(2)
(3)	(3)

Lesson 1 Summary
The Golden Age of Athens

(*A Message of Ancient Days* pp. 362–368)

Thinking Focus: Why were the years of Pericles' leadership called the Golden Age of Athens?

The Age of Pericles

Pericles had fled from Athens just before the Persians invaded the city. Once the Greeks defeated the Persians, Pericles returned. Pericles was intelligent. He was also a persuasive speaker. He convinced people that his ideas were important. In 460 B.C., he was elected as a general. Being a general was one of the main offices in Athenian democracy.

Pericles had three goals for Athens:

- To protect the city, Pericles built a strong sea wall and trained a powerful navy.
- To make Athens the most beautiful city in the world, Pericles built new public buildings and temples. The most famous buildings are on a hill in the middle of Athens called the Acropolis.
- To strengthen Athenian democracy, Pericles spread power more evenly between the rich and the poor.

Pericles led Athens from 460 to 429 B.C. During this time, Athens became a center for art, literature, and ideas. The period became known as the Golden Age of Athens.

? What were Pericles' three major goals for Athens?

*Summary continues
on next page*

Life in a Citizen Family

Most Athenian men spent the day at the **agora**, a public marketplace. Some went to the marketplace to debate the important ideas of the day. Others were merchants. Athenian men also sometimes went to the public court to serve as jurors.

Women stayed at home, spinning wool, dying thread, and making fabric. They ground grain and baked bread. They also took care of their children. Athenian boys went to school after age seven. Girls stayed at home to learn household tasks. Women were seen in public with their husbands for only two events: plays and religious festivals.

Most people of Athens lived in mud-brick houses with windows facing an open courtyard. The homes of rich and poor looked much alike.

? How did the citizens of Athens spend their days?

agora
(ăg′ə-rə)
a marketplace in ancient Greece used as a meeting place

Life for Noncitizens

Noncitizens included metics and slaves. Noncitizens did much of the work in Athens. Metics, who came from other city-states, could not own property. But they could attend plays and religious festivals. They also had the right to use the law courts. Some became rich and returned to their home city-states.

Unlike metics, slaves had no legal rights. Many were treated well by their owners, however. Slaves farmed the land. Some slaves worked in goldsmithing or pottery making. These slaves were often paid for their work. They could sometimes earn enough to buy their freedom.

Some Athenian slaves worked in the silver mines. They led terrible lives. They often worked 10-hour shifts while chained to rocks. Many died from overwork or disease.

? How was a metic's life different from a slave's?

CHAPTER 12

Lesson 2 Preview
The Peloponnesian War

(*A Message of Ancient Days* pp. 369–373)

Athens Before and After the War

Causes
- Plague in Athens
- Athens's slave labor runs off.
- Allies join Sparta.
- Athenians leave ships unprotected.

Athens loses Peloponnesian War.

Effects
- Golden Age of Athens ends.
- Democracy declines.

1. **Study the graphic overview. Then complete the statements below.**

   a. The graphic overview shows why Athens lost the

   _____ and what happened as a result.

   b. One thing that caused Athens to lose the war was

   _____.

   c. Because Athens lost the war, _____

   _____.

2. **Study the map on page 370. Then complete the sentences below.**

   a. Macedonia was an ally of _____.

   b. Chios is in the _____ Sea.

   c. Rhodes was an ally of _____.

   d. Allies of _____ were divided geographically by

   allies of _____.

CHAPTER 12

Lesson 2 Reading Strategy
The Peloponnesian War

(*A Message of Ancient Days* pp. 369–373)

Cause and Effect This reading strategy helps you to understand events and why they occur. As you read, think about the factors that caused an event. Then think about what the effects of that event might be.

1. **Read the first paragraph under "Athens and Sparta" on pages 369. What caused Sparta to be afraid of Athens? Put a check mark next to the correct answer.**

   ___ Athenian democracy, as strengthened under Pericles, made Sparta nervous.

   ___ Athens had formed an alliance, which gave it increasing power.

   ___ A plague broke out in Athens, and Sparta was afraid it would spread.

2. **Read "Athens During the War" on pages 370 and 371. Why did Persia decide to give funds to Sparta to strengthen its navy?**

   _____

3. **Read "End of the War" on page 371. What happened when the Athenians went ashore at Aegospotami?**

   _____

4. **Read "End of the Golden Age" on pages 372 and 373. Then write a cause or an effect to complete the chart.**

Causes	Effects
	Spartan leaders decided to spare the city of Athens.
Socrates taught students to question things.	

Lesson 2 Summary
The Peloponnesian War

(*A Message of Ancient Days* pp. 369–373)

Thinking Focus: Why did the Golden Age come to an end?

Athens and Sparta

After the Persian Wars, Athens had formed an **alliance** with other city-states. Its purpose was to protect against invasions from Persia. But Athens soon took over the alliance. Athens began to create an empire by attacking cities outside Greece.

Sparta felt threatened by Athens's growing military power. In 431 B.C., Sparta insisted that Athens free the cities under its control. That is when the Peloponnesian War began.

Sparta began attacking farms surrounding Athens. Walls protected Athens itself, so Pericles called for everyone to come inside the walls. This caused overcrowding. Then a **plague** hit Athens. One in every four people died, including Pericles. Athens was weakening. Some of the city's allies joined forces with Sparta. The war continued for another 10 years. Then Persia gave money to Sparta for a new fleet of ships. In 405 B.C., Sparta captured the Athenian naval fleet and cut off the city's food supply. Athenians were starving. In 404 B.C., Athens surrendered.

[?] What caused the Peloponnesian War, and what were its consequences?

alliance
(ə-lī′əns)
a formal union among governments

plague
(plāg)
a highly contagious widespread disease that is often fatal

Summary continues on next page

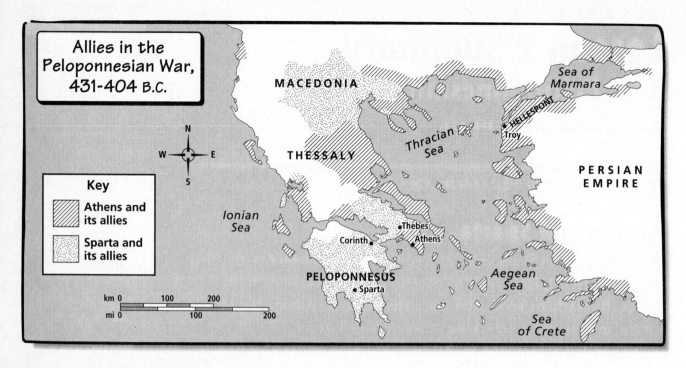

End of the Golden Age

The Peloponnesian War had lasted for 27 years. Spartan leaders spared the city of Athens. But they destroyed its democracy and set up rule by a few harsh rulers, called tyrants. These rulers were forced out within a year, and democracy was restored. But it wasn't the old democracy that had united Athens during the Golden Age. Many young Athenians didn't want to take part in public affairs.

Socrates was a great **philosopher** and teacher in Athens during this time. He wanted his students to question their lives and their world. Many Athenian leaders thought Socrates was making others challenge the government. They had Socrates arrested and sentenced him to die. At age 70, Socrates did not want to break the law by trying to escape. He died, drinking poison given him by officers of the government. Plato, a student of Socrates, went on to write about the teachings of his teacher and friend.

? Why did the teachings of Socrates upset Athenian leaders?

philosopher
(fĭ-lŏs′ə-fər)

a person who seeks learning through questioning and discipline

CHAPTER 12
Lesson 3 Preview
Alexander the Great and His Influence

(*A Message of Ancient Days* pp. 374–381)

The Spread of Greek Culture

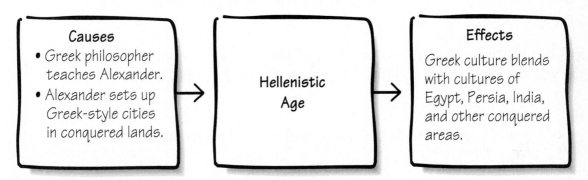

1. **Study the graphic overview. Then complete the sentences below.**

   a. The graphic overview shows the causes and effects of

   _____.

   b. One of the _____ of the Hellenistic Age was that Alexander set up Greek-style cities in lands he conquered.

   c. The blending of Greek culture with other cultures was an

   important _____.

2. **Look at the map on page 381, and read the caption. Use the map to complete the sentences below.**

   a. Alexander's empire stretched from Greece and Macedonia in the west to the _____ River in the east.

   b. After Alexander's death, the empire was divided into

   _____ smaller empires.

   c. The largest of these was ruled by _____.

   d. Libya, Egypt, and the lands at the eastern end of the Mediterranean Sea were ruled by _____.

CHAPTER 12

Lesson 3 Reading Strategy
Alexander the Great and His Influence

(*A Message of Ancient Days* pp. 374–381)

Sequence This reading strategy helps you follow what is happening in your reading. As you read, pay attention to dates and times, as well as to words such as *before*, *finally*, *after*, and *then*.

1. **Read the entire section called "The Rise of Macedonia" on page 375. Then put these events in order by writing 1, 2, and 3 in the blanks.**

    ___ Philip became ruler of Greece.

    ___ Philip defeated tribes to the north and west of Macedonia.

    ___ Philip became king of Macedonia.

2. **Read the first paragraph under "Alexander's Conquests" on page 375. Write the sentence that tells what Alexander did AFTER he put down the revolts. Circle the word that helps you understand the sequence.**

    _____

3. **Read "After Alexander" on page 381. Then number these events to show to order in which they happened.**

    ___ Alexander died of a fever at the age of 33.

    ___ Alexander's generals split up his empire.

    ___ Alexander created the largest empire in the western world.

4. **Complete the timeline below by looking through the lesson to find the dates.**

    Phillip becomes king of
    Macedonia

    Alexander succeeds Philip

    Alexandria, Egypt, is
    founded

Lesson 3 Summary
Alexander the Great and His Influence

(*A Message of Ancient Days* pp. 374–381)

Thinking Focus: How did Alexander the Great spread Greek culture throughout the ancient world?

The Rise of Macedonia

From 399 B.C. to 338 B.C., many Greek city-states fought to gain power over others. None was as powerful as Athens had once been. Then, in 359 B.C., King Philip became ruler of Macedonia, a city-state north of Greece. He strengthened Macedonia's army. He invented stronger weapons and better battle plans. Philip used his powerful army to build an empire throughout Greece. By 338 B.C., he had become ruler of Greece. He quickly combined the Greek army with his own. Then, as he was setting out to conquer Persia, King Philip was murdered.

[?] How did Macedonia become a powerful state?

Alexander's Conquests

At the age of 20, Alexander took charge of his father's kingdom. He put down rebellions that sprang up. Then he began his **conquest** of new lands. He and his armies traveled throughout Africa and Asia, taking over other peoples by force.

[?] How did Alexander build an empire?

conquest
(kŏn′kwĕst′)
the defeat of a nation or group, usually by force

Summary continues on next page

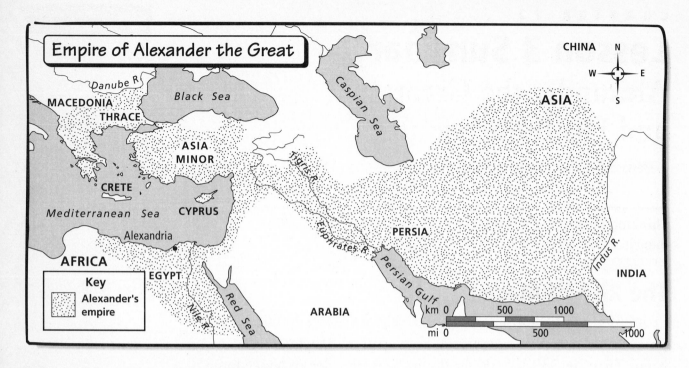

The Spread of Greek Culture

Alexander loved Greek culture. As he conquered new lands, he built cities like those in Greece. Many people learned to speak Greek and to read Greek literature. But Alexander also adopted features of the cultures he conquered. This time is known as the "Hellenistic Age." **Hellenistic** culture was a blend of Greek and Eastern cultures.

In 332 B.C., Alexander founded a new center for Greek culture. The city, located in Egypt, was named Alexandria. A great library was built there. The library remained an important intellectual center for about 700 years.

[?] What is Hellenistic culture?

> **Hellenistic**
> (hel′S-nis′tik)
> Greek-like; culture and history from the time of Alexander the Great to 146 B.C.

After Alexander

After his death at age 33, no leader was strong enough to take Alexander's place. His generals split the empire into many kingdoms. Finally, after many bloody battles, five generals took control of different parts of the empire. But no one part ever equaled in size or power the empire of Alexander the Great.

[?] Why did Alexander's empire decline after his death?

CHAPTER 12
Lesson 4 Preview
Contributions of the Greeks

(A Message of Ancient Days pp. 383–387)

Greek Art and Culture

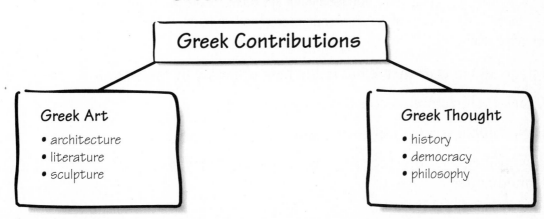

Greek Contributions

Greek Art
- architecture
- literature
- sculpture

Greek Thought
- history
- democracy
- philosophy

1. **Look at the graphic overview. Then use the information in it to complete this outline.**

I. Greek Art

   A. _____

   B. _____

   C. _____

II. Greek Thought

   A. _____

   B. _____

   C. _____

2. **Look at the photograph on page 383, and read the caption. Then look back at the photograph of the Parthenon on page 364. Write a few sentences explaining how the buildings on the Philadelphia riverfront show the influence of Greek architecture.**

_____

_____

_____

_____

CHAPTER 12
Lesson 4 Reading Strategy
Contributions of the Greeks

(*A Message of Ancient Days* pp. 383–387)

Summarize This reading strategy helps you remember key points about what you have read. When you get to a good break in your reading, stop and write down the main ideas of what you have read.

1. **Read page 383 in your text. What is the best summary of this page?**

   ___ Greek architecture has been copied in many places.

   ___ Philadelphia is a beautiful city.

   ___ The influence of the ancient Greeks is found throughout the United States.

2. **Read "Greek Arts" on pages 384 and 385. What is the best summary of the effects of Greeks arts on the world?**

   ___ The Greeks set a standard for historical writing.

   ___ The literature, painting, sculpture, and historical writings had a major impact on the history of western civilization.

   ___ Many Greeks plays and poems are still read today.

3. **Read "Greek Ideas" on pages 386 and 387. Write down two of the ideas developed by the Greeks.**

   _____

   _____

4. **Now write a summary of Greek contributions to civilization.**

   _____

   _____

   _____

   _____

   _____

Lesson 4 Summary
Contributions of the Greeks

(*A Message of Ancient Days* pp. 383–387)

Thinking Focus: How does the culture of ancient Greece still influence our lives today?

Greek Arts

Greek styles have influenced building in many countries for the past 2,000 years. The most obvious feature of Greek style is the use of columns to support a roof.

Many forms of literature can be traced to the Greeks. The Greeks did not invent these forms, but they did perfect them. One form was the epic poem, a long poem about brave deeds. Another form was **lyric poetry**. A lyric poem is short. It deals with personal feelings. One of the greatest contributions of the Greeks was theater. Greek dramatists wrote both tragedies and comedies, many of which are still performed today.

Greek artists were among the first to show the human body in a lifelike way. Greek historians were the first to write factual accounts of past events. In fact, the Greek historian Herodotus is known as the "father of history."

? What are three forms of literature that the Greeks are famous for?

lyric poetry
(lǐ′rĭk pō′ĭ-trē)
poems that express personal emotions

Summary continues on next page

Cultural Contributions of the Greeks

Writing

Lyric poems
Epic poems
Histories
Theater and drama

Culture and Arts

Life-like sculptures
Architecture
Democracy

Philosophy

Teachings by Socrates,
Plato, Aristotle

Math and Science

Medicine
Geometry
Astronomy

Greek Ideas

Greek philosophers and scientists raised many questions about the world. Philosophers like Socrates, Plato, and Aristotle developed ways of finding answers that are still used today. Greek scientists made discoveries about astronomy, medicine, and mathematics. The Greek astronomer Aristarchus suggested that the earth revolved around the sun. The mathematicians Pythagoras and Euclid made discoveries in geometry. Hippocrates, a doctor, wrote a pledge that medical doctors still take today. Greek ideas about art, science, democracy, and government have been passed down through the centuries. That is why Greek culture is called the "starting point" of Western civilization.

[?] How did Greek philosophers and scientists react to and try to understand the natural world?

Chapter Overview
The Rise of Rome

Fill in the blank spaces below with information from the chapter.

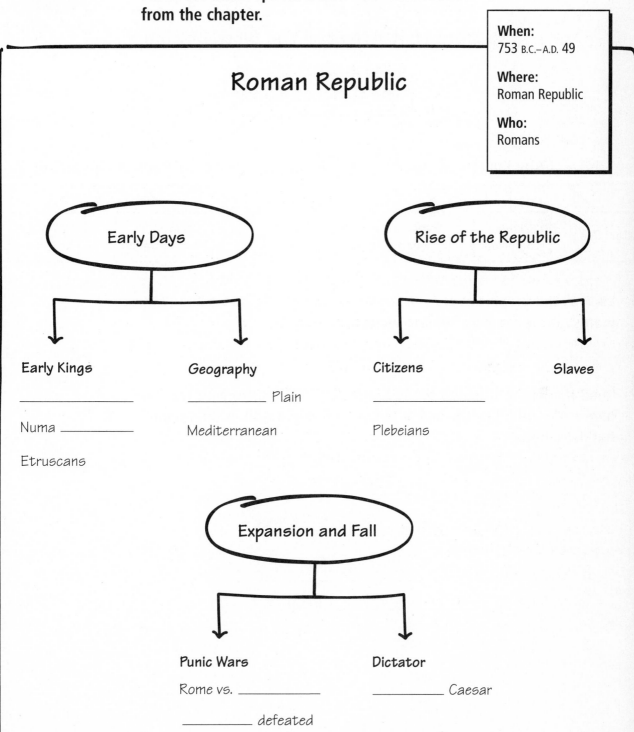

Roman Republic

When:
753 B.C.–A.D. 49

Where:
Roman Republic

Who:
Romans

Early Days

Rise of the Republic

Early Kings

_____

Numa _____

Etruscans

Geography

_____ Plain

Mediterranean

Citizens

_____

Plebeians

Slaves

Expansion and Fall

Punic Wars

Rome vs. _____

_____ defeated

Dictator

_____ Caesar

CHAPTER 13

Lesson 1 Preview
The Birth of Rome

(*A Message of Ancient Days* pp. 396–399)

Factors that Affected the Birth of Rome

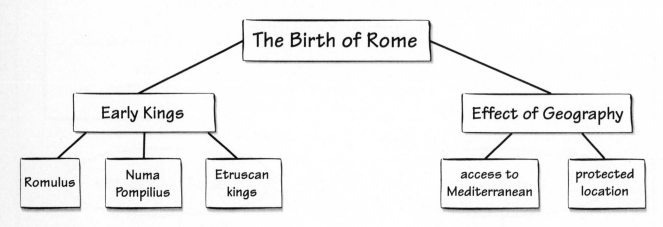

1. Look at the graphic overview. Suppose you were to add a box with the words "on seven hills." Where would you add it?

   _____

2. Read the lesson title and the red and blue headings in your text, pages 396–399. Use the words in the headings to fill in the lesson outline below.

   I. The Birth of Rome

      A. Seven Kings

         1. Rome's _____ Kings

         2. The Etruscans

      B. Midpoint of the _____

         1. The _____ Plain

         2. The _____ of Latium

CHAPTER 13

Lesson 1 Reading Strategy
The Birth of Rome

(*A Message of Ancient Days* pp. 396–399)

Using the Visuals This reading strategy helps you use photographs, maps, charts, and illustrations to help you understand what you read. As you read, be sure to study the visuals and carefully read the captions.

1. **Look at the photograph of the Etruscan fresco on page 397, and read the caption. What can you learn from this picture?**

   ___ The Etruscans painted many different subjects.

   ___ The Etruscans were advanced at showing movement of the human body.

   ___ Etruscan women did not play musical instruments.

2. **Look at the inkwell on page 398, and read the caption. What important thing does this object reveal about Etruscan civilization?**

   ___ Etruscan writers used ink.

   ___ The Etruscans had many different types of inkwells.

   ___ The Etruscan alphabet was much like ours.

3. **Study the map on the bottom of page 398. What do the red and green colors represent on the map?**

   _____

4. **Study the map on page 399. Fill in the chart to show which roads lead to which hills outside of Rome.**

Roads	Hills
	Mount Albanus
Via Latina	Mount Alginus
Via Tiburtina	

Lesson 1 Summary
The Birth of Rome

(A Message of Ancient Days **pp. 396–399)**

Thinking Focus: How was Rome founded, and how did it grow?

Seven Kings

Much of the early history of Rome comes to us through legends. According to legend, Rome was founded in 753 B.C. by Romulus, who became Rome's first king. Romulus started Rome's army and government. The second king was Numa Pompilius. He brought peace to the city and, according to legend, started the Roman religion. Both kings were advised by a **Senate** made up of people from Rome's leading families. Each king chose priests from among the members of the Senate. The king and his priests performed religious duties and interpreted **omens.**

About 575 B.C., the Etruscans from the north took over Rome and ruled for 66 years. They taught the Romans the Etruscan alphabet and new ways of building. Rome, once a city of straw huts, became a walled city of fine buildings. There were paved streets, a huge arena, and a vast sewer system. In 509 B.C., the people of Rome overthrew their last king, the cruel Tarquin the Proud.

? How did the Etruscans influence the Romans?

Senate
(sĕn´ĭt)

in ancient Rome, the advisors to the Republic and later to the empire

omen
(ō´mən)

a thing or event that is believed to foretell something

Summary continues on next page

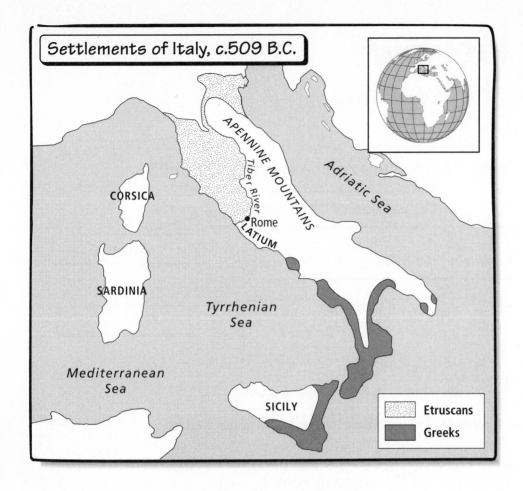

Settlements of Italy, c.509 B.C.

CORSICA

APENNINE MOUNTAINS

Tiber River

Rome

LATIUM

Adriatic Sea

SARDINIA

Tyrrhenian Sea

Mediterranean Sea

SICILY

Etruscans

Greeks

Midpoint of the Mediterranean

At the time of the early kings, Rome was one of many city-states in Italy. To the north lay the Etruscan city-states. To the south lay Greek settlements. Rome was located near the center of the Italian peninsula on a broad plain known as Latium. Romans spoke Latin, and most Romans worked as herders and farmers of wheat, grapes, or olives.

Rome's location was a good one for many reasons. It was built on seven hills, so it was easy to defend. It was on the Tiber River, so products could be shipped easily in and out of the city. The river led to the Mediterranean Sea, which was only 15 miles away. Rome was located at the center of the Mediterranean world, with Greece to the east, Spain to the west, and Africa to the south. In time, the Roman Empire would expand to all of these areas.

? What part did geography play in the development of Rome?

CHAPTER 13

Lesson 2 Preview
The Rise of the Republic

(A Message of Ancient Days pp. 406–411)

Social Structure of the Roman Republic

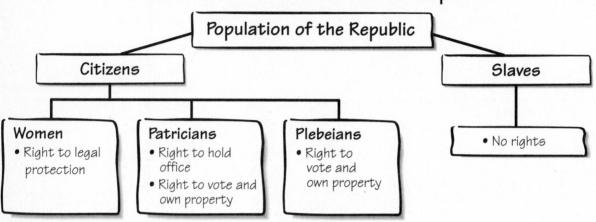

1. **Look at the graphic overview. Then complete the statements below.**

   a. Both the _____ and the

      _____ had the right to vote.

   b. Only the patricians had the right to _____.

   c. The only group that had no rights was the

      _____.

   d. _____ were entitled to legal protection.

2. **Study the chart on Roman government on page 410. Complete the sentences below.**

   a. There were two consuls, one _____ and one

      _____.

   b. Citizen Assemblies included all adult _____
      citizens.

   c. In the "middle level," plebeians were either

      _____ or _____.

Date:

Lesson 2 Reading Strategy
The Rise of the Republic

(*A Message of Ancient Days* pp. 406–411)

Self-Question   This reading strategy helps you stay focused on what you read. Ask yourself questions before you read a section. Then read to see if you can find the answer to your questions.

1. **Look at the main head "Patricians and Plebeians" on page 406. Which question do you think will be answered as you read the section?**

   ___ What countries were these two groups from?

   ___ What was the difference between a patrician and a plebeian?

   ___ Did patricians and plebeians live at the same time?

2. **Look at the chart on page 410, and read the caption. Which question do you think might be answered as you read the section "Roman Government"?**

   ___ What did the different government officials do?

   ___ Were there other branches in the Roman government?

   ___ Why weren't women eligible for government positions?

3. **Read "Roman Government" to see if the question you chose was answered. Then fill in the paragraph below.**

> ### What I Learned
>
> The consuls carried on the daily business of the government and commanded the
> _____ . The Senate was made up of _____
> citizens. The Senate controlled the _____ and foreign policy.

Lesson 2 Summary
The Rise of the Republic

(*A Message of Ancient Days* pp. 406–411)

Thinking Focus: What internal and external struggles occurred during the rise of the Roman Republic?

Patricians and Plebeians

In 509 B.C., the Romans set up a new form of government called a **republic** and elected leaders called **consuls**. Roman citizens were divided into two groups. **Patricians** were a small group of people from wealthy families. **Plebeians** were ordinary citizens. Both patricians and plebeians could vote. But only patricians could hold office. So patricians held all the power.

Plebeians were divided between rich and poor. If a poor plebeian had to borrow money from a rich one, he was forced into **debt bondage**. He became a servant of the citizen to whom he owed money. Yet another division in Roman society was between citizens and slaves.

? What were the differences between patricians and plebeians in the early Republic?

Struggle for Rights

In 494 B.C., the plebeians formed their own assembly and elected their own officials, called tribunes. The patricians could not survive without the plebeians to do work. So they let the plebeians keep their assembly and their tribunes. The plebeians also wanted Roman laws to be written down. In 450 B.C., the Roman laws were engraved on 12 bronze tablets for all to see. During the 300s B.C., plebeians gained the right to become priests and members of the Senate. Debt bondage was outlawed. Still, patrician laws applied to everyone, but plebeian laws applied only to plebeians. The patricians finally agreed that all Romans would be treated equally under Roman law.

? What were the major steps in the plebeians' struggle for greater rights?

republic
(rĭ-pŭb′lĭk)

a nation in which citizens have power to elect leaders and representatives

consul
(kŏn′səl)

either of two elected officials of the ancient Roman Republic

patrician
(pə-trĭsh′ən)

a member of the small class of wealthy families in ancient Rome

plebeian
(plĭ-bē′ən)

a member of the large class of ordinary citizens in ancient Rome

debt bondage
(dĕt bŏn′dĭj)

in ancient Rome, the condition in which a poor person became a servant to a wealthy person to whom he owed money

Summary continues on next page

Roman Government

The Roman government was headed by two consuls. In 367 B.C., it was decided that one consul had to be a plebeian. Consuls were elected for one year. One consul could veto the action of the other. The consuls ran the government and the army. They were advised by the Senate, which was made up of 300 citizens. Senators were chosen for life. The Senate controlled the treasury and foreign policy. Citizen assemblies had to approve the laws proposed by the Senate. These assemblies also elected the consuls.

? How was the government of the Roman Republic organized?

Early Expansion

Outside of Rome, the army was expanding the area under Roman control. By 275 B.C., Rome had gained control of the whole Italian peninsula. Rome was successful in part because it made allies of each group of people it conquered. These allies were offered protection and a share in the profits from future victories. By 270 B.C., Rome had more citizens and well-trained soldiers than any power in the Mediterranean world.

? What made the Romans successful conquerors?

Name: _____   Date: _____

Lesson 3 Preview
Overseas Expansion

(A Message of Ancient Days pp. 412–418)*

The Punic Wars

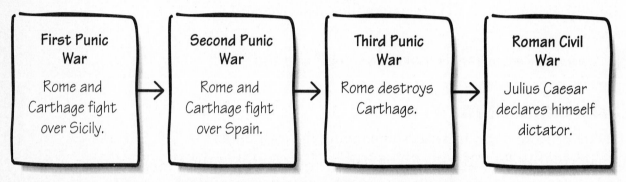

First Punic War — Rome and Carthage fight over Sicily. → Second Punic War — Rome and Carthage fight over Spain. → Third Punic War — Rome destroys Carthage. → Roman Civil War — Julius Caesar declares himself dictator.

1. **Look at the graphic overview. Then answer the following questions:**

   a. What four wars are represented in the graphic overview?

   _____

   _____

   b. What two places did Rome and Carthage fight to control?

   _____

   c. Which war resulted in dictatorship?

   _____

2. **Study the map on page 413. Then complete the sentences below.**

   a. A red star shows that the battle at Ilipa in Spain in 206 B.C. was a victory for _____.

   b. Corsica and Sardinia are bordered in red because they were conquered by _____ in _____.

   c. The purple areas show the _____ territories at the beginning of the _____ Punic War.

CHAPTER 13

Lesson 3 Reading Strategy
Overseas Expansion

(*A Message of Ancient Days* pp. 412–418)

Sequence This reading strategy helps you follow what is happening in your reading. As you read, pay attention to dates and times, as well as to words such as *before, finally, after,* and *then.*

1. **Read "The Punic Wars" on pages 412–415. Put these events in order by writing 1, 2, and 3.**

    ___ Under Hamilcar and Hannibal, Carthage expanded its empire in Spain.

    ___ Rome sold the people of Carthage into slavery and destroyed the city.

    ___ Rome and Carthage went to war for control of Sicily.

2. **Read the first paragraph under "Conquest of the Eastern Mediterranean" on page 415. What clue word helps you understand the sequence of Rome's conquests?**

    _____

3. **Read "Trouble at Home" on pages 416 and 417. Put these events in order.**

    ___ Farmers returned from war to find slaves are working their land

    ___ More than 100,000 slaves revolted against Roman masters.

    ___ Farmers left their land to fight in the Punic Wars.

4. **Read all of pages 417 and 418. Complete the information below by filling in the blanks.**

    73 B.C. — _____ gathers slave army.

    59 B.C. — Caesar is elected consul.

    49 B.C. — Caesar crosses the _____.

    _____ — Caesar becomes dictator.

Lesson 3 Summary
Overseas Expansion

(*A Message of Ancient Days* pp. 412–419)

Thinking Focus: How was Rome able to control the Mediterranean world?

The Punic Wars

While Rome was conquering Italy, another strong power existed in North Africa. This was the city of Carthage, which had trading posts all around the Mediterranean. Rome and Carthage fought three wars over who would control the Mediterranean. These wars were called the Punic Wars.

The First Punic War was fought over control of the island of Sicily. The Romans won and gained control of Sicily. During the Second Punic War, a brilliant leader from Carthage named Hannibal attacked Rome from the north, across the Alps. The Roman general Scipio Africanus finally defeated Hannibal after many bloody battles. After the Third Punic War, Rome destroyed Carthage and sold its survivors into slavery.

? What were the Punic Wars?

Conquest of the Eastern Mediterranean

By 50 B.C., Greece, Spain, Gaul, Asia Minor, and North Africa had become Roman provinces. Here is why Rome was able to conquer so many areas so quickly:

- Romans were proud of their republic and quick to defend it.
- Rome treated the people it conquered as allies.
- Rome's army was much stronger than most others.
- Roman leaders valued victory highly and rewarded victors.
- Wars were a source of great wealth to Rome and its citizens.

? How could Rome conquer so much of the Mediterranean so quickly?

*Summary continues
on next page*

Trouble at Home

Rome's battles were often fought by farmer-soldiers. As the empire expanded, they had to leave their farms for long periods of time. Soldiers who had left their farms often did not have the money to start them up again. Many landless farmers moved to the city, but could not find jobs there.

Rome's large population of slaves caused other problems. Slaves were often treated brutally in Rome. In 73 B.C., a slave named Spartacus formed a huge army of slaves. For two years, the slave army fought the Roman army. Eventually, Spartacus was killed and 6,000 of the slaves were crucified.

? What problems did Rome have at home?

Fall of the Roman Republic

By 50 B.C., the wealthy people in Rome had become even wealthier. But there were also more poor people and more slaves. Many poor citizens joined the army because they could find no other jobs. They fought for money, not for Rome. Soldiers fighting for money were loyal only to the generals who paid them. And the generals began to compete with each other for control of the government.

One former consul, Julius Caesar, became a general. He took his troops into Gaul and won control of the people there. Several other generals resented his successes. When Caesar marched his troops back to Rome, civil war broke out. In 46 B.C., Caesar defeated his rival, Pompey, and declared himself **dictator**.

? Who was Julius Caesar?

> **dictator**
> (dĭk′tā′tər)
> a ruler who has absolute power

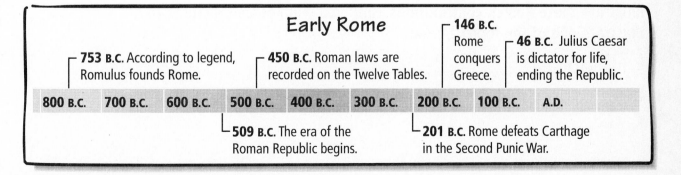

Early Rome

753 B.C. According to legend, Romulus founds Rome.

450 B.C. Roman laws are recorded on the Twelve Tables.

146 B.C. Rome conquers Greece.

46 B.C. Julius Caesar is dictator for life, ending the Republic.

| 800 B.C. | 700 B.C. | 600 B.C. | 500 B.C. | 400 B.C. | 300 B.C. | 200 B.C. | 100 B.C. | A.D. | |

509 B.C. The era of the Roman Republic begins.

201 B.C. Rome defeats Carthage in the Second Punic War.

CHAPTER 13

Lesson 4 Preview
Greece and Rome

(A Message of Ancient Days pp. 420–424)

Greek Influence and Roman Genius

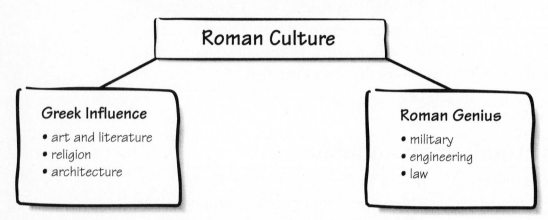

1. **Look at the graphic overview. Then answer the questions below.**

   a. The Romans were influenced by the Greeks in several ways. What were three of these ways?

   _____

   _____

   b. The Romans also made many contributions of their own. In what three areas did the Romans excel?

   _____

   _____

2. **Look at the pictures on pages 421, 422, and 424 of your text. Next to each of the words below, list any pictures and their page numbers that illustrate these Roman contributions. Hint: you will not find pictures to illustrate one of the topics below.**

   a. military _____

   b. engineering _____

   c. law _____

CHAPTER 13

Lesson 4 Reading Strategy
Greece and Rome

(*A Message of Ancient Days* pp. 420–424)

Compare and Contrast This reading strategy helps you understand how events are similar and different. As you read about historical events, think about how they compare and contrast with events you already know.

1. **Read the section "Greek Influence on Rome" on pages 420–421. Pay special attention to the Greek gods that were given different names by the Romans. Fill in the chart below.**

deity	Greek name	Roman name
ruler of the gods		
goddess of love		
god of war		

2. **Read the section "Military Organization" on pages 421–422. Write a sentence comparing the Roman and Greek armies.**

_____

_____

3. **Name two ways in which Greece and Rome were similar.**

_____

_____

4. **Name two ways in which Greece and Rome were different.**

_____

_____

Lesson 4 Summary
Greece and Rome

(A Message of Ancient Days pp. 420–424)

Thinking Focus: How strong was Greece's influence on Rome?

Greek Influence on Rome

The Romans borrowed heavily from Greek culture. In fact, the Romans were so influenced by the Greeks that the result is called Greco-Roman culture. The Romans worshiped Greek gods and gave them Roman names. Roman writers got their inspiration from Greek writers. Roman children learned Greek literature by heart. Roman builders adopted Greek forms of buildings. They used columns in building their temples, just as the Greeks had.

[?] What is Greco-Roman culture?

Roman Genius

The Romans owed much to Greek culture. But they also became extremely skillful in three areas:

Roman Achievements

Military organization
The Romans had one of the greatest armies the world had ever seen.

Engineering skill
The Romans used concrete and the arch to build huge public projects like bridges, aqueducts, and stadiums.

Legal administration
The Roman legal system was based on common sense, fairness, and individual rights.

Summary continues on next page

The Roman army was a great military force. The army was divided into legions, with 6,000 soldiers in a legion. The soldiers were well-trained and disciplined. Soldiers enlisted for 20 years, so they became hardened fighters. There was a strict chain of command. And each legion was self-sufficient, so that it could fight long battles in faraway places without returning to Rome for supplies.

The Romans built more than 50,000 miles of roads. The roads were useful to the army. They also helped in trade and communication. The Romans perfected the arch, and they invented concrete. With arches and concrete, the Romans built huge bridges, **aqueducts**, and stadiums. The Romans also developed the science of surveying.

Roman laws were first written on the Twelve Tables in 450 B.C. Over time, the Romans developed a legal system with courts, judges, and lawyers. Many modern-day legal systems are based on the practices of Roman law.

? At what skills did the Romans excel?

aqueduct
(ăk′wĭ-dŭkt′)

a bridgelike structure built to carry water from a distant source

Chapter Overview
The Roman Empire

Fill in the blank spaces below with information from the chapter.

When:
49 B.C.–A.D. 235

Where:
Roman Empire

Who:
Romans

Roman Society

The Early Empire
· _____
· Trajan
· Hadrian
· Marcus Aurelius

Social Rank
· Elite
· _____
· _____
· Freedmen

Pax Romana

Daily Life
· Home
· _____
· Religion
· _____

The Roman Economy
· Agriculture
· Industry
· _____

CHAPTER 14
Lesson 1 Preview
The Early Empire

(A Message of Ancient Days **pp. 430–435)**

The Early Roman Empire

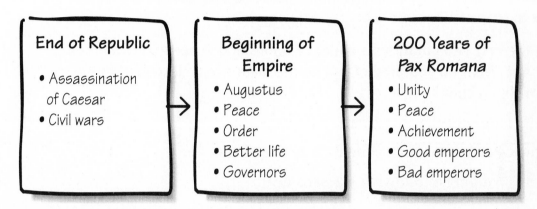

End of Republic
- Assassination of Caesar
- Civil wars

Beginning of Empire
- Augustus
- Peace
- Order
- Better life
- Governors

200 Years of Pax Romana
- Unity
- Peace
- Achievement
- Good emperors
- Bad emperors

1. **Use the graphic overview to answer the following questions:**

   a. Which came first: the Republic of Rome or the Roman Empire?

   _____

   b. Was the end of the republic a time of peace or of war?

   _____

   c. What one thing characterized both the beginning of the empire and 200 years of *Pax Romana*?

   _____

2. **Look at the timeline on page 434 of your text. Use it to complete the following sentences:**

   a. The 200 years of *Pax Romana* began under the rule of _____.

   b. *Pax Romana* ended with the rule of _____.

   c. The Roman Empire expanded to its greatest size under the rule of

   _____.

CHAPTER 14
Lesson 1 Reading Strategy
The Early Empire

(*A Message of Ancient Days* pp. 430–435)

Predict/Infer This reading strategy helps you understand what you have read and what you will read next. Before you read a section, think about the titles, pictures, and captions. Then think about what will happen in the selection.

1. **Read the first two paragraphs under "Establishing Peace and Order" on page 431. What do you predict will be the main event described in the rest of this section?**

   ___ the failure of the assassination attempt

   ___ how Brutus became the new dictator of Rome

   ___ the civil unrest following Caesar's death

2. **Read "The Empire of Augustus" on pages 431 and 432. Then look at the other subheads in this section of the lesson. What do you predict the next sections will be about?**

   ___ the emperors who ruled after Augustus

   ___ how the empire became strong under Augustus

   ___ why Augustus proved to be a weak leader

3. **Give a reason for the prediction you just chose. Then read the last paragraph in this section to confirm your prediction or to revise it.**

   _____

   _____

4. **Read the first paragraph of "Unifying the Empire" on page 434. Then write your prediction about what will be discussed in the rest of this section.**

   _____

   _____

   _____

Lesson 1 Summary
The Early Empire

(A Message of Ancient Days pp. 430–435)

Thinking Focus: How did the Romans build a powerful and prosperous empire?

Establishing Peace and Order

Many Roman senators believed that Julius Caesar wanted to be king. They did not want him to have this much power, so they made plans to **assassinate** him. But after killing Caesar, the senators had to hide from angry mobs who felt that Caesar had improved their lives. A struggle for power followed. Finally, Caesar's son, Octavian, became emperor of Rome in 27 B.C. Octavian was later given the title "Augustus," meaning "respected one."

Augustus was a strong and popular leader. He controlled the military. He also appointed the officials who governed the **provinces.** Augustus built or restored 82 temples in the city of Rome. He set up a police force, a fire brigade, and a department to supply food to the people. Augustus's reign was the beginning of a period known as the *Pax Romana,* a time of peace and unity for the empire.

assassinate
(ə- săs′ə-nāt′)
to murder someone, especially for political reasons

province
(prŏv′ĭns)
in the Roman Empire, any of the lands outside Italy ruled by the Romans

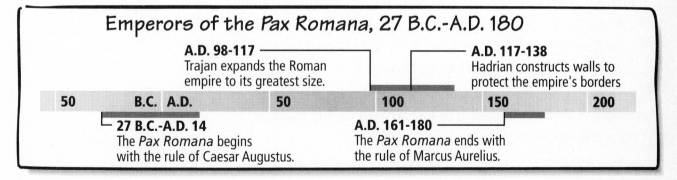

Emperors of the *Pax Romana,* 27 B.C.-A.D. 180

A.D. 98-117 —
Trajan expands the Roman empire to its greatest size.

A.D. 117-138 —
Hadrian constructs walls to protect the empire's borders

| 50 | B.C. | A.D. | 50 | 100 | 150 | 200 |

27 B.C.-A.D. 14
The *Pax Romana* begins with the rule of Caesar Augustus.

A.D. 161-180 —
The *Pax Romana* ends with the rule of Marcus Aurelius.

❓ What did Augustus do for the city of Rome and for the provinces?

Summary continues on next page

Ruling the Empire

After Augustus died, four dynasties ruled the Roman Empire. Augustus started the tradition of family rule by choosing his stepson, Tiberius, to succeed him. The dynasty begun by Augustus ended with the reign of Nero in A.D. 68. Nero showed little interest in governing the empire and was disliked by the Roman people. When a bloody civil war broke out, Nero killed himself. Another unpopular emperor was Domitian, who ruled during the second dynasty. A cruel and ruthless leader, Domitian was assassinated in A.D. 96.

A third dynasty of "good emperors" included many effective leaders.

- Trajan expanded the empire to its greatest size.
- Hadrian built walls to protect the empire's borders.
- Marcus Aurelius protected the empire's borders.

The death of Marcus Aurelius marked the end of the *Pax Romana*. Emperors who followed were unable to control such a vast empire.

[?] How did the reigns of the "good emperors" contrast with the reigns of Nero and Domitian?

Unifying the Empire

Over the centuries, Rome had conquered peoples with many different languages and customs. The Roman emperors unified these peoples in three ways:

- They encouraged conquered peoples to build cities modeled on Rome. These cities had a central square, or forum, and temples for Roman gods. The people living in the cities learned Latin and came to think of themselves as Romans.

- They allowed some of the conquered people to become Roman citizens. They were protected by Roman law, and they could do business and own property.

- They allowed governors to continue ruling their provinces.

[?] What policies did the Roman emperors follow in order to unify the empire?

Lesson 2 Preview
Social Rank in the Empire

(A Message of Ancient Days pp. 436–439)

Three Social Classes

	Elite	More Humble	Slaves
Rank in Society	Most powerful	ordinary citizens	human property
Number	less than 2%	most free men and women	as much as 33% of Roman Italy
Occupations	senators, officials	farmers, laborers, shopkeepers, soldiers	

1. **The graphic overview gives information about the three social classes in ancient Rome. Use it to answer the questions below.**

   a. Which class had the fewest people? _____

   b. Which group had the most people? _____

   c. To which class did most women belong?

   _____

   d. To which class did government leaders belong?

   _____

2. **Look at the visual, and read the caption, on page 437 of your text. Then complete the sentences below.**

   a. The seats closest to the field are occupied by the

   _____ .

   b. The _____ stood in the top tier.

   c. Today, seating is determined by the price of admission. In Roman times, seating was determined by _____ .

CHAPTER 14

Lesson 2 Reading Strategy
Social Rank in the Empire

(*A Message of Ancient Days* pp. 436–439)

Evaluate This reading strategy helps you recognize the difference between facts and opinions. A fact is something that can be proven to be true. An opinion is a belief based on what a person thinks or feels.

1. **Read "Three Social Classes" on pages 437 and 438. Which statement below is an opinion?**

    ___ The emperor appointed members of the elite class to serve as government officials.

    ___ It was wrong for slaves on farms to work so hard.

    ___ The more humble class included most of the free men and women in the empire.

2. **Write three other facts from the section "Three Social Classes."**

    _____

    _____

    _____

3. **Read "A Roman Dinner Party" on pages 438 and 439. Decide if the statement below is a fact or an opinion. Write *fact* or *opinion* after the statement.**

    Eating in a reclining position is considered a mark of excellence.

    _____

4. **Read "Changes in Social Level" on page 439. Then, write your opinion of the fact below.**

    Wealthy Romans sometimes helped their former slaves start a business.

    My Opinion: _____

    _____

Lesson 2 Summary
Social Rank in the Empire

(A Message of Ancient Days pp. 436–439)

Summary also on
Audiotape

Thinking Focus: What role did social rank play in Roman life?

Three Social Classes

Roman society had three classes: the **elite**, the "more humble," and the slaves. A person's class was decided by birth and by wealth. Class determined what people wore and what jobs they could do. It even determined where they sat in the Colosseum, Rome's giant outdoor stadium.

Members of the elite were wealthy and powerful. They even had special legal rights. Some of the "more humble" were fairly wealthy. Others, however, were poor. Slaves were considered human property. They could be bought or sold—or even given their freedom. Slaves who became free were called "freedmen." Some freedmen became very powerful in Rome.

elite
(ĭ-lēt')
in ancient Rome, the upper class

Classes of Roman Society

Class	Made up of	Seats in the Colosseum	Jobs
elite	government officials, senators, wealthy citizens	best seats, close to the action	government, law, farm ownership
"more humble"	ordinary citizens, freed men and women	seated above the elite, farther from the action	farming, the military, shopkeeping
slaves	1/3 of the people of Roman Italy	seats at the very top	housework, farm labor, mining, shipping, roadbuilding

? How did life differ for people in the three different social classes?

Summary continues on next page

Reading Support Resources

Lesson Summary • **Chapter 14, Lesson 2** **213**

© Houghton Mifflin Company. All rights reserved.

The Importance of Social Level

At a Roman dinner party, the classes of society were treated very differently. The most honored may have been given better food and wine than the others. Members of the elite might ridicule the clothes or behavior of those in lower classes. Dinner was served by slaves who could be punished for the slightest mistake.

Social divisions were clearly defined in ancient Rome. But sometimes, people were able to improve their social position by gaining wealth. Moving up in the class system was probably most difficult for farmers, who made up the vast majority of the "more humble" class. They had little chance of ever becoming rich. Soldiers were sometimes able to earn promotions to better-paying positions. Slaves could better themselves by buying their freedom. With the help of former owners, some freed slaves even started their own businesses.

? How could Romans improve their social position?

CHAPTER 14

Lesson 3 Preview
Daily Life in Ancient Rome

(*A Message of Ancient Days* pp. 440–446)

Rich Romans and Poor Romans

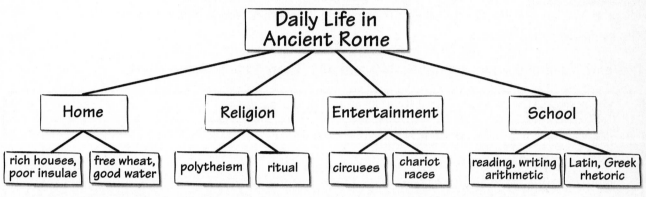

1. **Look at the graphic overview. Use it to answer the following questions:**

   a. What might a Roman boy study at school?

   _____

   b. The prefix *poly-* means "many." What does this tell you about the religion of the Romans?

   _____

   c. What did the government provide for poorer Romans?

   _____

2. **Look at the pictures on page 441 of your text. Find at least one additional picture in the lesson that gives information about daily life in ancient Rome. Write the page number(s) and explain your choice(s).**

   _____

   _____

   _____

   _____

   _____

   _____

CHAPTER 14

Lesson 3 Reading Strategy
Daily Life In Ancient Rome

(A Message of Ancient Days pp. 440–446)

Compare and Contrast   This strategy helps you understand how events are similar and different. As you read about historical events, think about how they compare and contrast with events you already know.

1. **Read "Rich and Poor" on pages 440 and 441. Then complete the chart.**

Rich People	Poor People
lived in large houses with many rooms	
owned many slaves	

2. **Read "Family Life in the Empire" on page 443. Then read the statement below. Write a contrasting statement about family life during the Roman Empire.**

   In the days of the Republic, the father arranged marriages for his children, or even sold them as slaves.

   _____

   _____

3. **Read "Entertainment" on page 444. Write a sentence comparing Roman entertainment with modern entertainment.**

   _____

   _____

4. **Read "Religious Practices" on pages 445 and 446. Write a sentence comparing the Roman religion to another religion practiced in Rome.**

   _____

Lesson 3 Summary
Daily Life in Ancient Rome

(A Message of Ancient Days **pp. 440–446)**

Thinking Focus: How was daily life different for rich and poor Romans?

Rich and Poor

A rich family in Rome might have a large house with many rooms. Some wealthy families had as many as 4,000 slaves. Slaves cooked, cleaned, and took care of the children. In some cases, a slave had only one job, such as hairdresser for the mistress.

For every wealthy home, there were 26 blocks of dark, dirty apartments of the poor. Some of these homes had only one room. There was no heat or running water. Fire, crime, and disease were serious problems. Children often died before they were 10 years old.

? How did the housing of the rich Romans compare with the housing of the poor?

Family Life in the Empire

By the A.D. 100s, most fathers were not as strict as they had been in the past. A father could no longer sell his children, nor could he force them to marry. Women had the freedom to own both property and slaves. Children of wealthy families went to small private schools. They learned reading, writing, and arithmetic. Girls had no formal education after age 15. Sons, however, were taught Latin, Greek literature, and **rhetoric**. Roman schools rarely offered advanced sciences. These subjects were learned through working with doctors or engineers.

? What were family life and schooling like for young people growing up in the Roman Empire?

rhetoric
(rĕt′ər-ĭk)

the art of effective writing and public speaking

Summary continues on next page

Benefits of Life in Rome

The city of Rome had the best and the worst of life in the Mediterranean world. Disease, crime, and fires were commonplace. But the emperors tried to keep the people happy. The government offered free wheat to the poor. Sometimes it offered money to those in need. The emperors also spent much money to entertain the people. Throughout the A.D. 100s, nearly one-third of the days in each year were holidays. On these days, the emperor provided huge circuses and games for the people. Chariot races, as well as bloody events like animal hunts and gladiator fights, brought people to the Colosseum regularly.

[?] How did the emperors provide "bread and circuses" for the people of Rome?

Religious Practices

On special days, Romans gathered to worship the gods Jupiter, Juno, and Minerva. At home, they worshiped household gods through daily offerings. In A.D. 126, they built a magnificent temple called the Pantheon.

The Roman state religion was based on **rituals**, or ceremonies, rather than on teaching people how to behave. The purpose of the rituals was to please the gods—and to be rewarded by them. But because the Roman religion did not teach people how to act, some people became dissatisfied with it. They started looking for other religions. Some people became Christians. At first there was tolerance of other religions in Rome. But once the empire started to decline, this tolerance ended.

> **ritual**
> (rĭch′oo-əl)
> a ceremony or rite

[?] What was the Roman state religion like, and why were some people dissatisfied with it?

CHAPTER 14
Lesson 4 Preview
The Roman Economy

(*A Message of Ancient Days* pp. 447–451)

Agriculture, Industry, and Trade in Ancient Rome

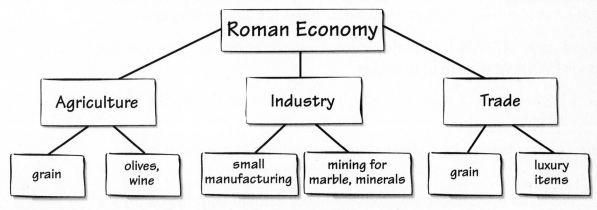

1. **Study the graphic overview. Use it to complete the sentences below.**

   a. The Roman economy depended on three things: agriculture,

      _____, and _____ .

   b. In addition to grain, Roman farmers produced

      _____ and _____ .

   c. Industry in ancient Rome included mining and

      _____ .

   d. Ancient Romans needed to engage in trade to get grain and

      _____ .

2. **Look at the pictures on pages 447–450 of your text. Explain how each picture illustrates one of the following features of the Roman economy: agriculture, industry, or trade.**

   _____

   _____

   _____

   _____

   _____

CHAPTER 14

Lesson 4 Reading Strategy
The Roman Economy

(*A Message of Ancient Days* pp. 447–451)

Finding the Main Idea This reading strategy helps you organize and remember what you read. When you finish a selection, jot down the main idea and its supporting details.

1. **Read page 447. Which sentence below best states the main idea of this page? Write *M* next to your choice.**

   ___ Roman trading ships carried olive oil and wine during the 200s B.C.

   ___ Archaeology is complicated process, but from it we can learn a lot.

   ___ Much has been learned from a sunken Roman ship found off the coast of Italy.

2. **Read "An Agricultural Economy" on pages 448 and 449. Which sentence best states the main idea of this section? Write *M* next to your choice.**

   ___ The economy of ancient Rome depended on agriculture.

   ___ Farmers in ancient Rome raised grain, olives, and grapes.

   ___ Modern industry employs many people because there is a big demand for manufactured items.

3. **Read the first paragraph "Manufacturing and Mining" on pages 450. Then complete the chart below by writing two supporting details for the main idea stated.**

Main Idea	Supporting Details
Mining was the largest industry in the Roman Empire.	1._____ _____ 2._____ _____

Lesson 4 Summary
The Roman Economy

(A Message of Ancient Days **pp. 447–451)**

Thinking Focus: What were some important products of the Roman economy, and why were they important?

An Agricultural Economy

Agriculture was important to the Roman economy. Olive oil and wine from Italy were shipped throughout the empire. But Roman farming methods were not very advanced, so crops were small. Four out of five people in the empire worked on farms. Farmers were forced to give most of their surplus grain to the government as taxes. Farmers were left with very little money to spend.

Most people in ancient Rome had only enough money for simple clothes and possessions. Only the wealthy could afford to buy fine jewelry and ornate pottery. There was a very small **market** for these manufactured items. Manufacturing plants in the empire remained small, with most work done by slaves.

❓ Why was Roman farming so poor?

market
(mär′kĭt)

the demand for goods; the opportunity to buy or sell

Trade in the Empire

Grain was the most important trade item in Rome. Wheat and barley were used for making bread, an important food in Rome. The land around Rome could not grow enough grain for the city's one million people. So Rome depended on grain imports from North Africa, Egypt, and Sicily. As many as 300,000 people in the city were too poor to buy grain. The government had to give grain to these people. It also had to feed another 300,000 soldiers stationed in the provinces.

The largest industry in the empire was mining. Marble was mined in Greece and Italy. Gold and silver came from Spain. Lead and tin were mined in Britain. Italian towns manufactured pottery, textiles, weapons, and tools for trade throughout the empire.

Summary continues on next page

Trade in luxury items made up a very small part of the economy. Ostrich eggs and ivory came from the Sahara. Silks, gems, and spices came from the East. This trade, of course, was not nearly as important as the trade for grain.

? Why did the Romans need to import grain?

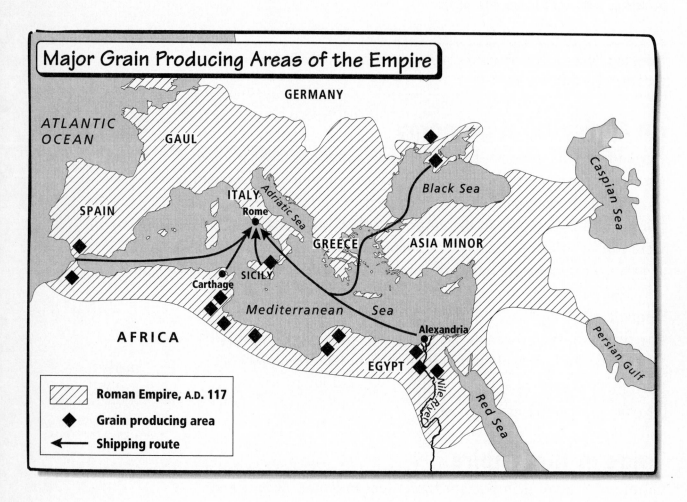

Major Grain Producing Areas of the Empire

GERMANY

ATLANTIC OCEAN

GAUL

SPAIN

ITALY

Adriatic Sea

Rome

GREECE

Black Sea

ASIA MINOR

Caspian Sea

SICILY

Carthage

Mediterranean   Sea

AFRICA

Alexandria

EGYPT

Nile River

Persian Gulf

Red Sea

▨ Roman Empire, A.D. 117

◆ Grain producing area

← Shipping route

Chapter Overview
Christianity and the Fall of Rome

Fill in the blanks with information from the chapter.

| When: |
| 36 B.C.–A.D. 476 |
| **Where:** |
| Rome |
| **Who:** |
| Jews, Christians, Pagans |

The Last Centuries of the Roman Empire

The Early Christians →

Roots of Christianity—Judaism
Spread of Christianity—Paul

Rome and the Christians →

Attack on Christianity
Rise of _____

The Decline of _____ →

End of Pax Romana
Reign of Diocletian
Reign of _____

_____ →

_____ Invasion
Causes of Fall

CHAPTER 15

Lesson 1 Preview
The Early Christians

(A Message of Ancient Days **pp. 458–462)**

Events in Early Christianity

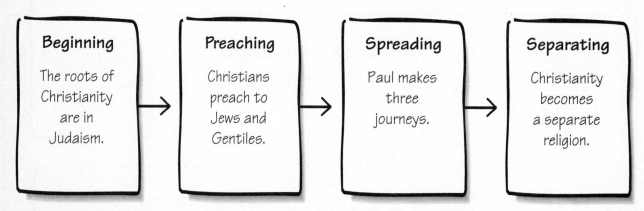

Beginning

The roots of Christianity are in Judaism.

Preaching

Christians preach to Jews and Gentiles.

Spreading

Paul makes three journeys.

Separating

Christianity becomes a separate religion.

1. **Study the graphic overview. Then read the statements below. Each of these statements is false. Rewrite each statement to make it true.**

   a. Judaism has roots in Christianity.

   _____

   b. Christians preached to Gentiles but not to Jews.

   _____

   c. Paul made two journeys.

   _____

   d. Christianity never became a separate religion.

   _____

2. **Look at the map on page 461 of your text and read the caption. Use this information to answer the following questions:**

   a. Name the two seas that Paul crossed on his second journey.

   _____

   b. Name two cities in Greece that Paul visited.

   _____

   c. Where did Paul go after visiting Ephesus?

   _____

Date:

Lesson 1 Reading Strategy
The Early Christians

(*A Message of Ancient Days* pp. 458–462)

Think About Words   This reading strategy helps you figure out the meaning of new words. When you come to an unfamiliar word, look for word parts you already know and use clues such as context and pictures.

1. **Read page 458. Then look at the picture on this page, and read the caption. How does this picture help you understand the meaning of the word** *conversion?*

    _____

2. **Now read the first paragraph on page 459. What words in this paragraph explain the meaning of conversion?**

    _____

3. **The word** *sect,* **in the first paragraph on page 459, may be unfamiliar to you. The author has included a synonym to help you understand the meaning of the word. Which word below is a synonym for** *sect?*

    ___ conversion

    ___ belief

    ___ group

4. **Read "Jews and Christians" on page 460. Also look at the illustrations on the page, and read the captions. Then write a synonym or a brief definition for each word in the chart.**

Word	Meaning
disciples	
diaspora	
Gentiles	
psalms	

Lesson 1 Summary
The Early Christians

(*A Message of Ancient Days* pp. 458–462)

Summary also on Audiotape

Thinking Focus: How were Judaism and early Christianity alike, and how were they different?

The New Faith

After the death of Jesus, Christianity remained a **sect** of Judaism. Judaism was one of many religions practiced in the Roman Empire. The Romans allowed religious freedom—so long as their gods were respected. But the Jews and Christians were not willing to worship these gods. They believed in one God. They lived by God's laws and by the teachings of the prophets.

In time, Christianity became a separate religion from Judaism. Both religions have had a lasting impact on Western civilization.

[?] How did the Jewish and Christian religious beliefs differ from those of the Romans?

sect
(sĕkt)
a division within a religious group

Gentile
(jĕn'tĭl')
one who is not of the Jewish faith

Jews and Christians

The first Christians were Jews. But unlike other Jews, they believed that Jesus was the Messiah. They believed that he had come to save the Jews—but not to save the **Gentiles**, or non-Jews. Peter, a disciple of Jesus, later suggested preaching the Christian gospel to Gentiles. Saul, who became known as Paul, carried that gospel throughout the Roman Empire.

Summary continues on next page

Reading Support Resources

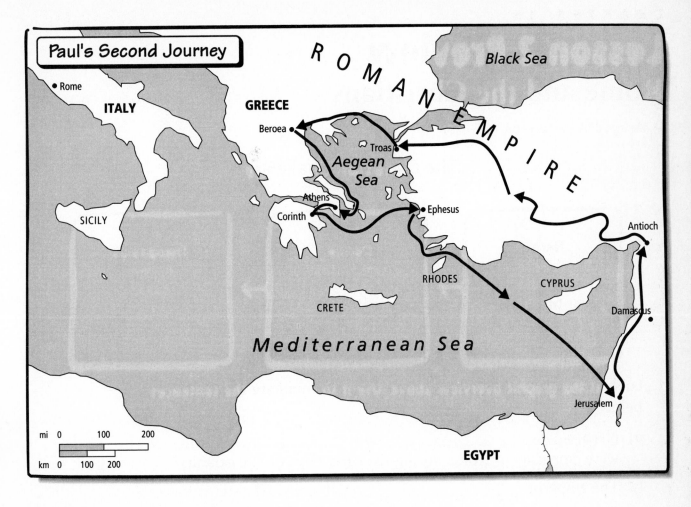

? Why did the Christians resist preaching to the Gentiles at first?

The Work of Paul

Paul had been a Roman citizen as well as a Jew. For several years, he was against those Jews who followed the teachings of Jesus. But then Paul had a vision. According to the New Testament, this vision led to his **conversion** to Christianity. After his conversion, Paul made three long journeys. He told people that if they accepted Jesus as the Christ, they could receive the love of God and eternal life. Because he was converting Romans, Paul was seen as a troublemaker. He was arrested and brought to Rome to stand trial. In A.D. 64, he was executed.

? How did Paul help spread Christianity?

persecute
(pûr′sĭ-kyōōt)

to punish; to treat harshly or cruelly

conversion
(kən-vûr′zhən)

a change in which one adopts a new religion

Name: _____   Date: _____

Lesson 2 Preview
Rome and the Christians

(A Message of Ancient Days pp. 463–469)

The Christian Challenge

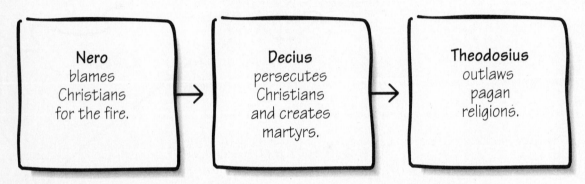

Nero blames Christians for the fire. → Decius persecutes Christians and creates martyrs. → Theodosius outlaws pagan religions.

1. **Look at the graphic overview above. Use it to complete the sentences below.**

   a. Nero, _____, and _____, were emperors of Rome during the early days of Christianity.

   b. The emperor _____ blamed Christians for a fire.

   c. The emperor _____ forbade the practice of pagan religions.

   d. Christians probably had the most difficult time under the rule of Emperor _____.

2. **Look at the illustration on page 464, and read the caption. What does it tell you about the persecution of the early Christians under Roman rule? Write two or three sentences about the picture.**

   _____

   _____

   _____

   _____

CHAPTER 15

Lesson 2 Reading Strategy
Rome and the Christians

(*A Message of Ancient Days* pp. 463–470)

Cause and Effect This reading strategy helps you understand events and why they occur. As you read, think about the factors that caused an event. Then think about what the effects of that event may be.

1. **Read page 463. Why did Nero give orders to kill Christians? Put a check mark next to the correct answer.**

   ___ He was violently opposed to Paul's converting the Gentiles.

   ___ He needed someone to blame for the big fire in Rome.

   ___ He feared that they would demand he give up the throne.

2. **Read the effect below. Based on what you just read, write a cause for this effect.**

   Cause:_____

   Effect: Christians were unpopular with most people in Rome.

3. **Read "The Attack on Christianity" on pages 467 and 468. Complete the chart below.**

Causes	Effects
Emperor Decius ordered all Christians to worship Roman gods.	Christians refused to follow his orders.
	Many Christians became martyrs.
Emperor Decius died in A.D. 251.	
Diocletian came to power.	

4. **Read "The Rise of Christianity" on pages 468 and 469. Write two effects that Constantine had on Christianity.**

   _____

Lesson 2 Summary
Rome and the Christians

(A Message of Ancient Days pp. 463–470)

Thinking Focus: How did Christianity grow between A.D. 64 and A.D. 400?

Rome's Early Response

At first the Romans didn't pay much attention to Christians. But in time they became suspicious. The Christians were different from other Romans. For example:

- They kept to themselves, almost like a secret club.
- They didn't care about worldly possessions.
- Many chose not to serve in the army.
- Religious services were private and held in Greek.

By A.D. 100, Roman law stated that anyone who admitted to being a Christian must be killed. Most Roman officials did not try to enforce this law. In extreme cases, Christians were made to fight lions as entertainment for Romans. However, most Christians lived in peace until A.D. 200.

? What was the attitude of the Romans toward the early Christians?

The Attack on Christianity

In A.D. 250, Emperor Decius demanded that all citizens worship Roman gods and make public sacrifices. He thought that this would please the gods and help end the problems within the empire. Decius ordered the execution of Christians who refused to obey. Some Christians chose death and became **martyrs**.

After Decius died in A.D. 251, the persecution ended for a few years. But when Valerian came to power, it resumed. It became even worse under Diocletian. Christian churches and crosses were destroyed. Sacred books were burned. Many Christians lost their jobs. Some were attacked and killed. This persecution continued until A.D. 311.

? Why and how did Decius, Diocletian, and other emperors persecute the early Christians?

martyr
(mär′tər)

a person who chooses to die rather than give up religious beliefs

Summary continues on next page

The Rise of Christianity

In A.D. 312, a Roman army leader named Constantine was about to go into battle. According to Christian historians, Constantine saw a vision of a cross. Constantine was not a Christian, but he believed that his men would win if they fought under the sign of Christ. He had his soldiers paint the cross on their shields. Constantine's army won the war, and he was made emperor. With Constantine's support, Christianity became the main religion of the Roman Empire. Constantine ended the persecution of Christians and rebuilt churches.

By the end of the A.D. 300s, church leaders had become powerful enough to give orders to emperors and even to punish them. For example, they could threaten **excommunication**. Just as Roman leaders had once persecuted Christians, now some fanatical Christians persecuted **pagans**, who were neither Christians nor Jews. As the Roman Empire weakened, Christianity had become a well-organized and powerful community.

? How did Constantine help Christianity become the main religion of the empire?

excommunication
(ĕks′kə-myōō′nĭ-kā′shən)

punishment that takes away membership in a church

pagan
(pā′gən)

to the early Christians, a person who is not a Christian or Jew

CHAPTER 15
Lesson 3 Preview
The Decline of Rome

(A Message of Ancient Days pp. 471–474)

Eastern and Western Roman Empires

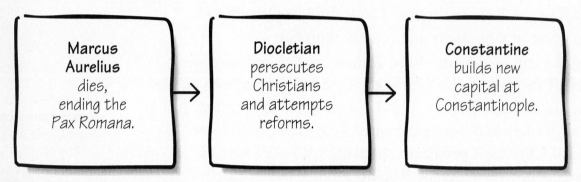

1. **Look at the graphic overview above. Use it to complete the sentences below.**

   a. With the death of _____, the *Pax Romana* ended.

   b. Two emperors who ruled after Marcus Aurelius were

   _____ and _____.

   c. During the reign of Diocletian, _____ were persecuted.

   d. Constantine made Christianity the main religion of Rome, and he

   _____.

2. **Look at the pictures, and read the captions, on pages 472 and 474. What do they tell you about the decline of the Roman Empire? Write one or two sentences about the pictures.**

   _____

   _____

   _____

   _____

CHAPTER 15
Lesson 3 Reading Strategy
The Decline of Rome

(*A Message of Ancient Days* pp. 471–474)

Compare and Contrast This reading strategy helps you understand how events are similar and different. As you read about historical facts, think about how they compare and contrast with events you already know.

1. **Read "The End of the *Pax Romana*" on pages 471 and 472. Write two statements contrasting the *Pax Romana* with the 50 years that followed.**

   _____

   _____

   _____

2. **Write a statement contrasting the price of wheat in Egypt in the early A.D. 200s and the late A.D. 200s.**

   _____

   _____

3. **Read "The Reign of Diocletian" and "The Reign of Constantine" on pages 472–474. Complete the chart, comparing and contrasting events under the two leaders.**

The Reign of Diocletian	The Reign of Constantine
Christians were persecuted.	
Government reorganization was begun.	
	A new capital was built at Constantinople.
Diocletian persecuted Christians.	

Lesson 3 Summary
The Decline of Rome

(*A Message of Ancient Days* pp. 471–474)

Summary also on Audiotape

Thinking Focus: Why did the Roman Empire begin to decline?

The End of the *Pax Romana*

The *Pax Romana* had been a 200-year period of peace and great achievement. It ended in A.D. 180 with the death of Emperor Marcus Aurelius. For the next several years, many different emperors ruled Rome. Some only ruled for a few months, and all but one were killed. During this time, the empire was under attack by various tribes. So taxes were raised to pay for a stronger army. Many people lost their jobs. There was too little food and much poverty.

? What problems did the empire face after the *Pax Romana?*

The Reign of Diocletian

In A.D. 284, the army made Diocletian emperor. Diocletian introduced major reforms. That is why his reign is called the "New Empire." His reforms included:

- issuing the **Edict** of Prices, which told farmers and merchants how much they could charge for various items;
- increasing the size of the army to fight off foreign threats;
- dividing the empire into regions to run the empire more efficiently;
- passing strict laws to keep people working so they could pay taxes.

Some of Diocletian's reforms worked, but they were costly and harsh. After he retired in A.D. 305, civil war broke out once more. Military leaders fought for power until Constantine finally took control.

? Why was Diocletian's reign called the "New Empire"?

edict
(ē′dĭkt)
a command

Summary continues on next page

The Reign of Constantine

Constantine reigned from A.D. 312–337. His major accomplishments include:

- establishing Christianity as the main religion in the empire;
- completing Diocletian's reorganization of the government;
- moving the capital from Rome to Constantinople.

The new capital, Constantinople, was built at the site of the ancient city of Byzantium. The location was excellent. It could be reached by both land and sea. It was easy to defend. By A.D. 330, Constantinople had become the "new Rome."

After Constantine's death, the empire declined further. By A.D. 400, it had been split into two parts. The Eastern Roman Empire would last for another 1,000 years. But the Western Empire was nearing an end.

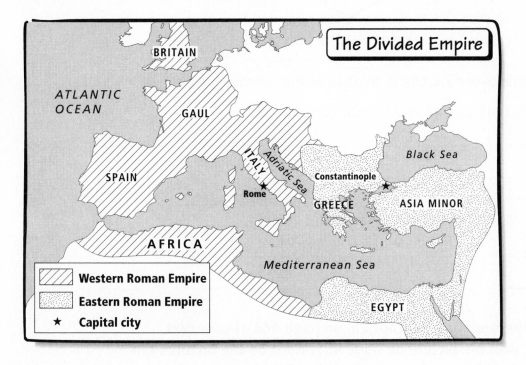

The Divided Empire

Legend:
- ▨ **Western Roman Empire**
- ▒ **Eastern Roman Empire**
- ★ **Capital city**

? What were the major accomplishments of Constantine?

Name: _____ Date: _____

Lesson 4 Preview
The Fall of Rome

(A Message of Ancient Days pp. 475–481)

Rome in Decline

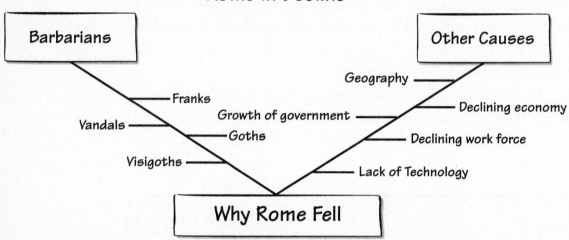

1. **Look at the graphic overview. Use it to answer the questions below.**

   a. Who were the barbarians? Name four different tribes.

   _____

   _____

   b. Rome fell because of barbarian invasions. But there were also other causes. What were two of these causes?

   _____

   _____

2. **Look at the picture, and read the caption, on page 468 of your text. Then compare it with the picture on page 481. What do the pictures tell you about important changes for early Christians? Write two or three sentences comparing the pictures.**

   _____

   _____

   _____

   _____

CHAPTER 15

Lesson 4 Reading Strategy
The Fall of Rome

(*A Message of Ancient Days* pp. 475–481)

Finding the Main Idea This reading strategy helps you organize and remember what you read. When you finish a selection, jot down the main idea and its supporting details.

1. **Read "Barbarian Invasions," which begins on page 476. Stop reading at the first subhead. Which sentence below best expresses the main idea of this section? Write *M* next to your choice.**

   ___ Barbarian tribes lived around boundaries of the Roman Empire in many different areas.

   ___ Numerous barbarian tribes challenged Roman control of the Empire over a 300-year period.

   ___ Romans looked down on the barbarians because they were different.

2. **Read "Growth of the Church," beginning on page 478 through the top of page 480. Which of the sentences below best expresses the main idea of the section? Write *M* next to your choice.**

   ___ As various barbarians tribes gained control of the Roman Empire, Christianity continued to grow.

   ___ St. Augustine wrote a book defending the role of Christianity.

   ___ The barbarians had no right to invade the Roman Empire.

3. **Read "Causes of the Fall" on pages 480 and 481. Then complete the chart below.**

Main Idea	Supporting Details

Lesson 4 Summary
The Fall of Rome

(*A Message of Ancient Days* pp. 475–481)

Thinking Focus: Why did the Roman Empire fall?

Barbarian Invasions

Since the time of the *Pax Romana,* the Roman Empire had been fighting off invasions. Romans called the invaders **barbarians**. Among the barbarians were the Franks, the Vandals, and the Goths. These groups were attracted by the empire's wealth. But they were also fleeing from other tribes that were moving into their territories from Asia.

Some emperors tried to fight off the invaders. Some tried to "buy" them off by giving them land or jobs in the army. In this way, the barbarians became part of the empire. In A.D. 378, the Visigoths revolted against the Romans. In A.D. 410, they marched into Rome. Barbarian chiefs took control of much of the western part of the empire. By A.D. 476, Rome had fallen.

? Who were the barbarians?

> **barbarian**
> (bär-bâr′ē-ən)
> in Roman times, a person from beyond the Roman frontier

Growth of the Church

Some Romans still blamed the empire's problems on the Christian church. They believed that the empire was crumbling because the Roman gods had been abandoned. St. Augustine, a church leader, responded to the Romans by writing *The City of God.* In this 22-volume book, St. Augustine explained that cities, like all worldly things, break down. But the city of God, which is spiritual, lasts forever.

? Why did St. Augustine write *The City of God?*

*Summary continues
on next page*

The Causes of the Fall

According to historians, there were several reasons for the fall of Rome. These include:

- the difficulty of defending weak western borders;
- the cost of supporting a big army and government;
- the waste of resources caused by civil wars;
- a decline in the work force due to a high death rate and fewer slaves;
- a lack of technology and machinery;
- military losses to barbarians.

? What were the major causes that led to the fall of Rome?

The Roman Legacy

After the Western Roman Empire fell, there was a period of decline that lasted 500 years. This period is known as the Early Middle Ages. Wars disrupted trade. The education system broke down. Most people were just trying to stay alive.

In Europe, the Christian church started **monasteries**, which included libraries that preserved the heritage of Rome. In the Eastern Roman Empire, scholars copied many Greek and Roman works. In this way, the ideas of Greco-Roman civilization were saved for future generations.

monastery
(mŏn′ə-stĕr′ē)
a home for people living under religious vows

? What were the Early Middle Ages?